GRADE
3

Ikenaga 2 Jos Leys

"A relatively simple formula can generate immensely complex images." – **Jos Leys**

3-D Geometry and Measurement   UNIT 9

Solids and Boxes

Investigations
IN NUMBER, DATA, AND SPACE®

Editorial offices: Glenview, Illinois • Parsippany, New Jersey • New York, New York
Sales offices: Boston, Massachusetts • Duluth, Georgia
Glenview, Illinois • Coppell, Texas • Sacramento, California • Mesa, Arizona

The Investigations curriculum was developed by TERC, Cambridge, MA.

This material is based on work supported by the National Science Foundation ("NSF") under Grant No. ESI-0095450. Any opinions, findings, and conclusions or recommendations expressed in this material are those of the author(s) and do not necessarily reflect the views of the National Science Foundation.

ISBN: 0-328-23752-3

ISBN: 978-0-328-23752-4

TERC

Co-Principal Investigators

Susan Jo Russell

Karen Economopoulos

Authors

Lucy Wittenberg
Director Grades 3–5

Karen Economopoulos
Director Grades K–2

Virginia Bastable
(SummerMath for Teachers,
Mt. Holyoke College)

Katie Hickey Bloomfield

Keith Cochran

Darrell Earnest

Arusha Hollister

Nancy Horowitz

Erin Leidl

Megan Murray

Young Oh

Beth W. Perry

Susan Jo Russell

Deborah Schifter
(Education
Development Center)

Kathy Sillman

Administrative Staff

Amy Taber
Project Manager

Beth Bergeron

Lorraine Brooks

Emi Fujiwara

Contributing Authors

Denise Baumann

Jennifer DiBrienza

Hollee Freeman

Paula Hooper

Jan Mokros

Stephen Monk
(University of Washington)

Mary Beth O'Connor

Judy Storeygard

Cornelia Tierney

Elizabeth Van Cleef

Carol Wright

Technology

Jim Hammerman

Classroom Field Work

Amy Appell

Rachel E. Davis

Traci Higgins

Julia Thompson

Collaborating Teachers

This group of dedicated teachers carried out extensive field testing in their classrooms, met regularly to discuss issues of teaching and learning mathematics, provided feedback to staff, welcomed staff into their classrooms to document students' work, and contributed both suggestions and written material that has been incorporated into the curriculum.

Bethany Altchek

Linda Amaral

Kimberly Beauregard

Barbara Bernard

Nancy Buell

Rose Christiansen

Chris Colbath-Hess

Lisette Colon

Kim Cook

Frances Cooper

Kathleen Drew

Rebeka Eston Salemi

Thomas Fisher

Michael Flynn

Holly Ghazey

Susan Gillis

Danielle Harrington

Elaine Herzog

Francine Hiller

Kirsten Lee Howard

Liliana Klass

Leslie Kramer

Melissa Lee Andrichak

Kelley Lee Sadowski

Jennifer Levitan

Mary Lou LoVecchio

Kristen McEnaney

Maura McGrail

Kathe Millett

Florence Molyneaux

Amy Monkiewicz

Elizabeth Monopoli

Carol Murray

Robyn Musser

Christine Norrman

Deborah O'Brien

Timothy O'Connor

Anne Marie O'Reilly

Mark Paige

Margaret Riddle

Karen Schweitzer

Elisabeth Seyferth

Susan Smith

Debra Sorvillo

Shoshanah Starr

Janice Szymaszek

Karen Tobin

JoAnn Trauschke

Ana Vaisenstein

Yvonne Watson

Michelle Woods

Mary Wright

Note: Unless otherwise noted, all contributors listed above were staff of the Education Research Collaborative at TERC during their work on the curriculum. Other affiliations during the time of development are listed.

Advisors

Deborah Lowenberg Ball,
University of Michigan

Hyman Bass, Professor of Mathematics and Mathematics Education
University of Michigan

Mary Canner, Principal, Natick Public Schools

Thomas Carpenter, Professor of Curriculum and Instruction,
University of Wisconsin-Madison

Janis Freckmann, Elementary Mathematics Coordinator,
Milwaukee Public Schools

Lynne Godfrey, Mathematics Coach,
Cambridge Public Schools

Ginger Hanlon, Instructional Specialist in Mathematics,
New York City Public Schools

DeAnn Huinker, Director, Center for Mathematics and
Science Education Research, University of Wisconsin-Milwaukee

James Kaput, Professor of Mathematics, University of
Massachusetts-Dartmouth

Kate Kline, Associate Professor, Department of Mathematics
and Statistics, Western Michigan University

Jim Lewis, Professor of Mathematics,
University of Nebraska-Lincoln

William McCallum, Professior of Mathematics,
University of Arizona

Harriet Pollatsek, Professor of Mathematics,
Mount Holyoke College

Debra Shein-Gerson, Elementary Mathematics Specialist,
Weston Public Schools

Gary Shevell, Assistant Principal,
New York City Public Schools

Liz Sweeney, Elementary Math Department,
Boston Public Schools

Lucy West, Consultant, Metamorphosis:
Teaching Learning Communities, Inc.

This revision of the curriculum was built on the work of the many authors who contributed to the first edition (published between 1994 and 1998). We acknowledge the critical contributions of these authors in developing the content and pedagogy of *Investigations*:

Authors

Joan Akers

Michael T. Battista

Douglas H. Clements

Karen Economopoulos

Marlene Kliman

Jan Mokros

Megan Murray

Ricardo Nemirovsky

Andee Rubin

Susan Jo Russell

Cornelia Tierney

Contributing Authors

Mary Berle-Carman

Rebecca B. Corwin

Rebeka Eston

Claryce Evans

Anne Goodrow

Cliff Konold

Chris Mainhart

Sue McMillen

Jerrie Moffet

Tracy Noble

Kim O'Neil

Mark Ogonowski

Julie Sarama

Amy Shulman Weinberg

Margie Singer

Virginia Woolley

Tracey Wright

Contents

UNIT 9

Solids and Boxes

Investigations

CURRICULUM

Overview of Program Components

FOR TEACHERS

The **Curriculum Units** are the teaching guides. (See far right.)

Implementing Investigations in Grade 3 offers suggestions for implementing the curriculum. It also contains a comprehensive index.

The **Resources Binder** contains all the Resource Masters and Transparencies that support instruction. (Also available on CD) The binder also includes a student software CD.

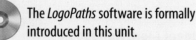

The *LogoPaths* software is formally introduced in this unit.

FOR STUDENTS

The **Student Activity Book** contains the consumable student pages (Recording Sheets, Homework, Practice, and so on).

The **Student Math Handbook** contains Math Words and Ideas pages and Games directions.

The *Investigations* Curriculum

Investigations in Number, Data, and Space® is a K–5 mathematics curriculum designed to engage students in making sense of mathematical ideas. Six major goals guided the development of the *Investigations in Number, Data, and Space*® curriculum. The curriculum is designed to:

- Support students to make sense of mathematics and learn that they can be mathematical thinkers

- Focus on computational fluency with whole numbers as a major goal of the elementary grades

- Provide substantive work in important areas of mathematics—rational numbers, geometry, measurement, data, and early algebra—and connections among them

- Emphasize reasoning about mathematical ideas

- Communicate mathematics content and pedagogy to teachers

- Engage the range of learners in understanding mathematics

Underlying these goals are three guiding principles that are touchstones for the *Investigations* team as we approach both students and teachers as agents of their own learning:

1. *Students have mathematical ideas.* Students come to school with ideas about numbers, shapes, measurements, patterns, and data. If given the opportunity to learn in an environment that stresses making sense of mathematics, students build on the ideas they already have and learn about new mathematics they have never encountered. Students learn that they are capable of having mathematical ideas, applying what they know to new situations, and thinking and reasoning about unfamiliar problems.

2. *Teachers are engaged in ongoing learning* about mathematics content, pedagogy, and student learning. The curriculum provides material for professional development, to be used by teachers individually or in groups, that supports teachers' continued learning as they use the curriculum over several years. The *Investigations* curriculum materials are designed as much to be a dialogue with teachers as to be a core of content for students.

3. *Teachers collaborate with the students and curriculum materials* to create the curriculum as enacted in the classroom. The only way for a good curriculum to be used well is for teachers to be active participants in implementing it. Teachers use the curriculum to maintain a clear, focused, and coherent agenda for mathematics teaching. At the same time, they observe and listen carefully to students, try to understand how they are thinking, and make teaching decisions based on these observations.

Investigations is based on experience from research and practice, including field testing that involved documentation of thousands of hours in classrooms, observations of students, input from teachers, and analysis of student work. As a result, the curriculum addresses the learning needs of real students in a wide range of classrooms and communities. The investigations are carefully designed to invite all students into mathematics—girls and boys; members of diverse cultural, ethnic, and language groups; and students with a wide variety of strengths, needs, and interests.

Based on this extensive classroom testing, the curriculum takes seriously the time students need to develop a strong conceptual foundation and skills based on that foundation. Each curriculum unit focuses on an area of content in depth, providing time for students to develop and practice ideas across a variety of activities and contexts that build on each other. Daily guidelines for time spent on class sessions, Classroom Routines (K–3), and Ten-Minute Math (3–5) reflect the commitment to devoting adequate time to mathematics in each school day.

About This Curriculum Unit

This **Curriculum Unit** is one of nine teaching guides in Grade 3. The ninth unit in Grade 3 is *Solids and Boxes.*

- The **Introduction and Overview** section organizes and presents the instructional materials, provides background information, and highlights important features specific to this unit.

- Each Curriculum Unit contains several **Investigations.** Each Investigation focuses on a set of related mathematical ideas.

- Investigations are divided into one-hour **Sessions,** or lessons.

- Sessions have a combination of these parts: **Activity, Discussion, Math Workshop, Assessment Activity,** and **Session Follow-Up.**

- Each session also has one or more **Classroom Routines and Ten-Minute Math** activities that are done outside of math time.

- At the back of the book is a collection of **Teacher Notes** and **Dialogue Boxes** that provide professional development related to the unit.

- Also included at the back of the book are the **Student Math Handbook** pages for this unit.

- The **Index** provides a way to look up important words or terms.

Overview

O F   T H I S   U N I T

Investigation	Session	Day	
INVESTIGATION 1 **Sorting, Describing, and Building Solids** Working with geometric solids, students learn to sort and describe them according to their attributes. They develop language to communicate effectively about solids and their attributes.	**1.1** Sorting Polyhedra	1	
	1.2 What's My Shape?	2	
	1.3 Building Polyhedra from Pictures or Models	3	
	1.4 Assessment: Building Polyhedra from Descriptions—Day 1	4	
	1.5 Building Polyhedra from Descriptions—Day 2	5	
INVESTIGATION 2 **Making Boxes** Students learn to recognize whether different patterns can be made into boxes.	**2.1** Making Boxes for a Cube	6	
	2.2 Patterns For 2-Cube Boxes	7	
	2.3 Patterns For Triangular Pyramids	8	
INVESTIGATION 3 **How Many Cubes in a Box?** Students figure out how many cubes can fit into a given box and make their own patterns for boxes.	**3.1** Finding the Number of Cubes in a Box	9	
	3.2 12-Cube Boxes	10	
	3.3 Assessment: Patterns from the Bottom Up	11	
	3.4 Riddles About Boxes	12	
	3.5 End-of-Unit Assessment	13	

Each *Investigations* session has some combination of these five parts: **Activity, Discussion, Math Workshop, Assessment Activity,** and **Session Follow-Up.** These session parts are indicated in the chart below. Each session also has one or more **Classroom Routines and Ten-Minute Math** activities that are done outside of math time.

Activity	Discussion	Math Workshop	Assessment Activity	Session Follow-Up		Practicing Place Value	More or Less?	Quick Images: 3-D
●	●			●		●		
● ●				●		●		
●	●			●		●		
●	●		●	●				
	●		●	●		●		
● ●	●			●			●	
●	●			●			●	
●	●			●			●	
● ●	●			●				●
●	●			●				●
● ●			●	●				●
	●	●		●				●
	●		●	●				●

Ten-Minute Math

Mathematics

Solids and Boxes is the second Grade 3 unit in the Geometry and Measurement strand of *Investigations*. These units help students develop ideas about the attributes of 2-D and 3-D shapes. Students come to understand how these attributes determine their classification. They also develop ideas about linear measurement (which includes perimeter), area, the measurement of angles, and volume.

LOOKING BACK In the early grades, students worked with Geoblocks (sets of wooden three-dimensional blocks related by volume) to begin the work of exploring, sorting, and describing three-dimensional geometric shapes. In Grade 2, students examined the Geoblocks and described their attributes. They sorted the blocks and matched them to footprints of their two-dimensional faces. As students worked on these activities, they learned to identify geometric terms for different shapes and for the attributes of shapes. They began to develop an understanding of the concept of volume as they put Geoblocks together to form larger blocks in the set.

This unit focuses on 3 Mathematical Emphases:

1 Features of Shape Describing properties of 3-dimensional shapes

Math Focus Points

- Describing the components and properties of different classes of solids such as polyhedra (3-D shapes having only flat surfaces, such as prisms and pyramids) and nonpolyhedra (such as cones and cylinders)
- Distinguishing between polyhedra and nonpolyhedra
- Distinguishing between prisms and pyramids
- Identifying the components of polyhedra (faces, edges, and vertices) and how they come together to form the whole
- Visualizing and building polyhedra by using knowledge of their components (faces, edges, and vertices) and how they come together to form the whole

In this unit, students sort and build common geometric solids so that they become familiar with what shapes make up these solids and how the shapes and solids are related. They begin to notice and describe important properties of the shapes (e.g., how many edges and faces a solid shape has, or how a pyramid has triangular faces coming to a point). They learn to distinguish between polyhedra (3-D shapes having only flat surfaces) and nonpolyhedra (3-D shapes that have curved surfaces), and to differentiate within the class of polyhedra, between prisms and pyramids. Students develop their own language to describe and compare these shapes while they are exposed to, and begin to use, the mathematical terms for the shapes and their components.

2 Features of Shape Translating between 2-dimensional and 3-dimensional shapes

Math Focus Points

- Determining the number and shapes of the faces of cubes and other rectangular prisms and how they come together to form the whole
- Designing patterns that make open boxes for a cube
- Designing patterns that make open boxes for 2-cube rectangular prisms
- Determining the number and shapes of the faces of a triangular pyramid and how they come together to form the whole
- Designing patterns that make nets for triangular pyramids
- Communicating about spatial relationships
- Decomposing images of 3-D shapes and then recombining them to make a given structure

In Investigation 2, students begin with 3-D figures (cubes and other polyhedra) and design open boxes and nets to hold these objects. These activities develop students' ability to move in both directions between 3-D objects and their 2-D representations, as they consider how the 2-dimensional faces of these polyhedra come together to form a 3-D shape. This ability is further developed in Investigation 3 as students determine the rectangular prisms that fit into a variety of open-box patterns and design their own boxes to hold various rectangular configurations of a given number of cubes.

In Investigation 3, students begin the Ten-Minute Math activity *Quick Images,* in which they look at 2-D images of a 3-D cube structure, form a mental image of the structure, and then build it with cubes. As they do this activity, students learn to organize and analyze visual images. They develop the concepts and language needed to analyze and communicate about spatial relationships.

3 Volume Structuring rectangular prisms and determining their volume

Math Focus Points

◆ Determining the number of cubes that will fit in the box made by a given pattern

◆ Designing patterns for boxes that will hold a given number of cubes

◆ Seeing that the cubes filling a rectangular prism can be decomposed into congruent layers

In Investigations 2 and 3 of this unit, students make open boxes from grid paper and investigate the number of cubes that fit inside their boxes. They look for relationships between the structure of rectangular boxes and the arrays of cubes that fit inside (e.g., that a box with a 2-unit by 3-unit bottom that is 3 units high can hold 3 layers of 6 cubes). Gradually, students learn to visualize the capacity of the boxes without actually filling them with cubes. Understanding the structure of these rectangular prisms is essential for students' later understanding of volume, but it is a difficult concept that can take students several years and much physical experience to develop.

Many adults solve problems similar to the box tasks in this unit by using a formula for determining volume: number of cubes = length × width × height. The way young children approach these problems may not match the formula. Many of your students will develop an approach based on finding

the number of cubes in one layer and adding the layers or multiplying by the number of layers. As students use skip counting, repeated addition, or multiplication to find the total number of cubes, they are modeling the problems in a general way and are developing an excellent foundation for later work with volume—including volume formulae.

See page 14 for the complete listing of the Math Focus Points for the Ten-Minute Math activities in this unit.

LOOKING FORWARD

In Grade 4, students deepen their understanding of the attributes of 3-D figures by describing and naming geometric solids and their components. They continue their work on representing 3-D shapes in 2-D, with a focus on perspective and how different views of a 3-D object come together to form the whole. Their work with volume focuses on determining the structure and volume of rectangular prisms constructed from cubes. In Grade 5, students continue to develop their understanding of volume. They determine a general method for finding the volume of any rectangular prism and explore volume of other solid shapes such as pyramids, cylinders, and cones.

Technology Note

Using The *LogoPaths* Software Students were formally introduced to the *LogoPaths* software in the 2-D Geometry and Measurement unit, *Perimeter, Angles, and Area,* the fourth unit in the Grade 3 sequence. We recommend that students continue to have access to the software **outside of math time** in order to return to *Feed the Turtle,* a *LogoPaths* activity, and to spend time with the *Free Explore* option. For information about the *LogoPaths* software and directions for *Feed the Turtle,* refer to the *Software Support Reference Guide* found on the CD. See **Part 5: Technology in *Investigations:* Calculators and Computers** in *Implementing Investigations in Grade 3:* Introducing and Managing the *LogoPaths* software in Grade 3.

Assessment

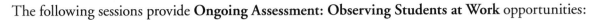

IN THIS UNIT

ONGOING ASSESSMENT: Observing Students at Work

The following sessions provide **Ongoing Assessment: Observing Students at Work** opportunities:

- **Session 1.1, p. 24**
- **Session 1.2, p. 31**
- **Session 1.3, p. 33**
- **Session 1.4, p. 39**
- **Session 1.5, p. 43**

- **Session 2.1, pp. 51 and 54**
- **Session 2.2, p. 58**
- **Session 2.3, p. 63**
- **Session 3.1, pp. 70 and 71**

- **Session 3.2, p. 77**
- **Session 3.3. pp. 82 and 84**
- **Session 3.4, pp. 87 and 89**
- **Session 3.5, p. 93**

WRITING OPPORTUNITIES

The following sessions have **writing** opportunities for students to explain their mathematical thinking:

- **Session 1.2, p. 31**
  Student Activity Book, p. 7

- **Session 1.5, p. 46**
  M14, *What's My Shape?*

- **Session 3.2, p. 79**
  Student Activity Book, p. 25

- **Session 3.3, p. 83**
  M32, Assessment: Writing About
  How Many Cubes

- **Session 3.4, p. 90**
  Student Activity Book, p. 31

- **Session 3.5, pp. 92, 93**
  M36, M38, End-of-Unit Assessment

PORTFOLIO OPPORTUNITIES

The following sessions have work appropriate for a **portfolio:**

- **Session 1.2, p. 31**
  Student Activity Book, p. 7

- **Session 1.4, p. 39**
  M12, Assessment Checklist: Building
  Polyhedra from Descriptions

- **Session 1.5, p. 46**
  M14, *What's My Shape?*

- **Session 3.3, pp. 81–82**
  M29–M31, Making Boxes from the
  Bottom Up

- **Session 3.3, p. 83**
  M32, Assessment: Writing About
  How Many Cubes

- **Session 3.4, p. 87**
  Student Activity Book, p. 29

- **Session 3.5, pp. 92–93**
  M36–M40, End-of-Unit Assessment

Assessing the Benchmarks

Observing students as they engage in conversation about their ideas is a primary means to assess their mathematical understanding. Consider all of your students' work, not just the written assessments. See the chart below for suggestions about key activities to observe.

 Checklist Available

Benchmarks in This Unit	Key Activities to Observe	Assessment
1. Identify and compare attributes of 3-dimensional solids.	**Session 1.2:** *What's My Shape?* **Session 2.2:** Patterns for 2-Cube Boxes	**Session 1.4 Assessment Activity:** Building Polyhedra from Descriptions—Day 1 ✓ **Session 3.5 End-of-Unit Assessment:** Problems 1A, 1B
2. Determine the number of cubes (volume) that will fit in the box made by a given pattern.	**Session 3.1:** Determining the Number of Cubes in a Box **Session 3.3:** Patterns from the Bottom Up	**Session 3.3 Assessment Activity:** Writing About How Many Cubes **Session 3.5 End-of-Unit Assessment:** Problems 2A, 2B
3. Design patterns for boxes that will hold a given number of cubes.	**Session 3.2:** Designing Boxes to Hold 12 Cubes	**Session 3.5 End-of-Unit Assessment:** Problems 3A, 3B

Relating the Mathematical Emphases to the Benchmarks

Mathematical Emphases	Benchmarks
Features of Shape Describing properties of three-dimensional shapes	1
Features of Shape Translating between two-dimensional and three-dimensional shapes	2 and 3
Volume Structuring rectangular prisms and determining their volume	2 and 3

Classroom Routines and Ten-Minute Math

IN THIS UNIT

The **Classroom Routines** and **Ten-Minute Math** activities, to be done in ten minutes outside of math class, are introduced in a unit and repeated throughout the grade. Specific directions for the day's activity are provided in each session. For the full description and variations of the Classroom Routines and Ten-Minute Math activities, see *Implementing Investigations in Grade 3*.

Activity	Introduced	Full Description of Activity and Its Variations
Classroom Routines: *What's the Temperature?*	Unit 1, Session 1.1	*Implementing Investigations in Grade 3*
Ten-Minute Math: *Practicing Place Value*	Unit 1, Session 1.1	*Implementing Investigations in Grade 3*
Ten-Minute Math: *More or Less?*	Unit 1, Session 2.3	*Implementing Investigations in Grade 3*
Ten-Minute Math: *Quick Images: 3-D*	Unit 4, Session 1.5	*Implementing Investigations in Grade 3*

What's the Temperature?

Students record the outside temperature every Wednesday morning on a chart and on a graph. They continue to practice reading charts and graphs, considering the relationship between them, and discussing changes in temperature over time.

Practicing Place Value

Students practice reading, writing, and saying numbers and identifying the value of digits in the number. They add and subtract multiples of 10 and examine how these operations increase or decrease the values of the digits in each place. They also break 3-digit numbers into 100s, 10s, and 1s in different ways.

Math Focus Points

◆ Recognizing and interpreting the value of each digit in 3-digit numbers

◆ Finding different combinations of a number, using only 100s, 10s, and 1s and recognizing their equivalence (i.e., 1 hundred, 3 tens, and 7 ones = 1 hundred, 2 tens, and 17 ones = 13 tens and 7 ones = 12 tens and 17 ones, etc.)

◆ Reading and writing numbers up to 1,000

◆ Adding multiples of 10 to, and subtracting multiples of 10 from 3-digit numbers

More or Less?

Students use estimation to determine whether the sum or difference of an arithmetic problem displayed for a brief time is "more or less than 200 (or $2.00) or 1,000 (or $10.00)." They share their estimates, and describe their thinking.

Math Focus Points

◆ Breaking apart, reordering, or combining numbers within a problem, for easier computation

◆ Using knowledge of place value and known combinations to estimate sums and differences

◆ Practicing addition and subtraction skills

Quick Images: 3-D

Students visualize and analyze images of 3-D geometric figures. After briefly viewing an image of a 3-D structure, students build it from the mental image they formed during the brief viewing.

Math Focus Points

◆ Organizing and analyzing visual images

◆ Developing language and concepts needed to communicate about spatial relationships

◆ Decomposing images of 3-D shapes and then recombining them to make a given structure

Practice and Review

Practice and review play a critical role in the *Investigations* program. The following components and features are available to provide regular reinforcement of key mathematical concepts and procedures.

Books	Features	In This Unit ...
Curriculum Unit	**The Classroom Routines** and **Ten-Minute Math** activities, to be done in ten minutes outside of math class, are introduced in a unit and repeated throughout the grade. Specific directions for the day's activity are provided in each session. For the full description and variations of the Classroom Routines and Ten-Minute Math activities, see *Implementing Investigations in Grade 3*.	• **All sessions**
Student Activity Book	**Daily Practice** pages in the *Student Activity Book* provide one of three types of written practice: **reinforcement** of the content of the unit, **ongoing review,** or **enrichment** opportunities. Some Daily Practice pages will also have Ongoing Review items with multiple-choice problems similar to those on standardized tests.	• **All sessions**
	Homework pages in the *Student Activity Book* are an extension of the work done in class. At times they help students prepare for upcoming activities.	• **Session 1.1** • **Session 3.1** • **Session 1.3** • **Session 3.2** • **Session 2.1** • **Session 3.3** • **Session 2.2** • **Session 3.4** • **Session 2.3**
Student Math Handbook	**Math Words and Ideas** in the *Student Math Handbook* are pages that summarize key words and ideas. Most Words and Ideas pages have at least one exercise.	• **Student Math Handbook, pp. 125–133**
	Games pages are found in a section of the *Student Math Handbook*.	• **No games are introduced in this unit.**

Differentiation

Supporting the Range of Learners

Sessions	1.1	1.2	1.3	1.4	1.5	2.1	2.2	2.3	3.1	3.2	3.3	3.4
Intervention	●	●	●	●	●	●			●		●	●
Extension				●	●		●	●		●		●
ELL	●	●		●			●					

Intervention

Suggestions are made to support and engage students who are having difficulty with a particular idea, activity, or problem.

Extension

Suggestions are made to support and engage students who finish early or may be ready for additional challenge.

English Language Learners (ELL)

In Unit 9, students learn how to describe, visualize, and build 3-dimensional shapes, as well as how to explain their processes. This unit includes language-based activities and discussions that might be challenging for them. You can support English Language Learners by previewing key vocabulary and concepts, letting them try some activities ahead of time, and helping them make picture dictionaries or other visual aids for reference throughout the unit.

During small-group activities, English Language Learners should be grouped with native English speakers so they can contribute to the task while hearing and using relevant vocabulary in conversation with their peers. Use gestures and point to relevant features as you use descriptive words and shape-related vocabulary. Is this shape *tall* or *short?* Can it *roll?* Does it have *flat edges?* How many *faces* does this one have? These shapes are the *same* because they both have *squares.* How are these shapes *different?*

Throughout the unit, students have repeated opportunities to hear and use relevant vocabulary words in context. In the End-of-Unit Assessments, they are also required to put these words in writing. You can prepare English Language Learners for these tasks by writing down the words of students, for both native English speakers and English Language Learners, during activities and discussions. You can also offer opportunities for English Language Learners to write down their ideas at various points throughout the unit, especially in relation to tasks that are similar to the End-of-Unit Assessment. If you think that an English Language Learner knows the material but can't write about it, you can modify the assessment by asking the student to describe his or her strategies instead of writing about them.

Working with the Range of Learners: Classroom Cases is a set of episodes written by teachers that focus on meeting the needs of the range of learners in the classroom. In the first section, *Setting up the Mathematical Community,* teachers write about how they create a supportive and productive learning environment in their classrooms. In the next section, *Accommodations for Learning,* teachers focus on specific modifications they make to meet the needs of some of their learners. In the last section, *Language and Representation,* teachers share how they help students use representations and develop language to investigate and express mathematical ideas. The questions at the end of each case provide a starting point for your own reflection or for discussion with colleagues. See *Implementing Investigations in Grade 3* for this set of episodes.

Mathematical Emphasis

Features of Shape Describing properties of 3-dimensional shapes

Math Focus Points

◆ Describing the components and properties of different classes of solids such as polyhedra (3-D shapes having only flat surfaces, such as prisms and pyramids) and nonpolyhedra (such as cones and cylinders)

◆ Distinguishing between polyhedra and nonpolyhedra

◆ Distinguishing between prisms and pyramids

◆ Identifying the components of polyhedra (faces, edges, and vertices) and how they come together to form the whole

◆ Visualizing and building polyhedra by using knowledge of their components (faces, edges, and vertices) and how they come together to form the whole

Sorting, Describing, and Building Solids

	Student Activity Book	Student Math Handbook	Professional Development: Read Ahead of Time	
SESSION 1.1　　　　p. 22				
Sorting Polyhedra Through sorting geometric solids, students learn about their components. They use characteristics of geometric solids to distinguish between polyhedra and nonpolyhedra and, within the classification polyhedra, between prisms and pyramids.	1–5	125, 126, 129–130	• **Mathematics in This Unit,** p. 10 • **Teacher Note:** Geometric Solids: Types and Terminology, p. 95 • **Dialogue Box:** Talking to Students About Sorting, p. 107 • **Part 4: Ten-Minute Math and Classroom Routines** in *Implementing Investigations in Grade 3:* What's the Temperature?	
SESSION 1.2　　　　p. 28				
What's My Shape? Students develop knowledge of the components of various geometric shapes as they ask questions to identify mystery figures. They develop language to effectively communicate about solids and their characteristics.	7	127–128	• **Dialogue Box:** Playing *What's My Shape?,* p. 108 • **Dialogue Box:** Building Common Vocabulary, p. 109	
SESSION 1.3　　　　p. 32				
Building Polyhedra from Pictures or Models Students build polyhedra while looking at pictures or models. They develop understanding of the structure of the shapes as they reflect on the parts of the figures and the relationships between those parts.	8–11	125–126, 127–128		

Classroom Routines and Ten-Minute Math

See page 14 for an overview.

What's the Temperature?
- Mount the thermometer outside the classroom window.
- Post the Date and Temperature chart and the Temperature graph in the classroom.

Practice Place Value
- No materials needed

Materials to Gather	Materials to Prepare
• **Chart paper**	• **Geometric solids** Label sets of 12 geometric solids with numbers according to the illustration on page 95. Use small adhesive labels. (1 set per group of 4–6) • **M7–M8, Family Letter** Make copies. (1 per student)
• **Geometric solids** (1 set per group of 4–6)	• **Chart paper** Write "Rules for Playing *What's My Shape?*" on chart paper and post while students play. See page 29 for a list of the rules.
• **Geometric solids** (1 set per group of 4–6)	• **M6, Building Kit Length Guide** Make copies. (as needed for volunteers or aides) • **M9–M10, Family Letter** Make copies. (1 per student) • **Building kits** If you do not have the Building kits from the materials kit, you will have to make them or use the kits you made in Unit 4, *Perimeter, Angles, and Area*. Make Building kits with plastic drinking straws, balsa strips, or thin dowels. Each kit should have 10 eight-inch lengths, 10 six-inch lengths, 20 five-inch lengths, 20 four-inch lengths, 15 three-inch lengths, and 10 two-inch lengths. Refer to Building Kit Length Guide (M6) for cutting your straws or sticks in the right lengths. • For connectors, use clay, playdough, STYROFOAM™, or florist's foam. If you are using hollow straws, you can use paper clips or pipe cleaners, bent and stuck inside the straw ends to connect two or more together. Each kit should contain enough material for about 20 connectors. • If possible, ask parent volunteers or classroom aides to help you. These kits should be saved for subsequent years. (1 per pair) • Build some of the polyhedra yourself to highlight problems that students will encounter.

Sorting, Describing, and Building Solids, *continued*

		Student Activity Book	Student Math Handbook	Professional Development: Read Ahead of Time	
SESSION 1.4	p. 37	8, 13–14	127–128		
Assessment: Building Polyhedra from Descriptions—Day 1 Students build polyhedra from written descriptions, using knowledge of the components of polyhedra and how they come together to form the whole.					
SESSION 1.5	p. 42	8, 13, 15	127–128, 129–130		
Building Polyhedra from Descriptions— Day 2 Students continue to build polyhedra from written descriptions.					

Materials to Gather	Materials to Prepare
• **T102, Building Polyhedra** 🖥 • **Geometric solids** (as needed) • **Building kits** (1 per pair) • **Student-built polyhedra**	• **T102, Building Polyhedra** 🖥 Build some of the polyhedra shown on the transparency following the descriptions to highlight issues that students will encounter. • **M12, Assessment Checklist: Building Polyhedra from Descriptions** ☑ Make copies. (as needed)
• **T102, Building Polyhedra** 🖥 • **M12, Assessment Checklist: Building Polyhedra from Descriptions** ☑ • **Geometric solids** (as needed) • **Building kits** (1 per pair)	• **M13, Geometric Solids** Make copies. (1 per student) • **M14, *What's My Shape?*** Make copies. (1 per student) • **Hexagonal pyramid** Use the materials from the building kit to construct a hexagonal pyramid (see page 45). Have this ready to show to the students during the Discussion portion of the session. (if needed)

🖥 Overhead Transparency   ☑ Checklist Available

Sorting Polyhedra

Math Focus Points

◆ Describing the components and properties of different classes of
solids, such as polyhedra (3-D shapes having only flat surfaces,
such as prisms and pyramids) and nonpolyhedra (such as cones
and cylinders)

◆ Distinguishing between polyhedra and nonpolyhedra

◆ Distinguishing between prisms and pyramids

Vocabulary	
prisms	edges
pyramids	faces

Today's Plan		Materials
ACTIVITY **① Sorting Solids**	🕐 👥 **40 MIN GROUPS**	• Geometric solids*; chart paper
DISCUSSION **② Thinking About Sorting Schemes**	🕐 👫 **20 MIN CLASS**	• Geometric solids
SESSION FOLLOW-UP **③ Daily Practice and Homework**		• *Student Activity Book*, pp. 1–5 • *Student Math Handook*, pp. 125, 126, 129–130 • M7–M8, Family Letter*

*See *Materials to Prepare*, p. 19.

Ten-Minute Math

Practicing Place Value Say "one hundred thirty-four," and ask students to write the
number. Make sure all students can read, write, and say this number correctly. Ask
students to solve these problems mentally, if possible:

- What is: 134 + 30?   134 + 40?   134 + 50?   134 + 100?
  134 + 200?   134 + 300?

Write each answer on the board. Ask students to compare each sum with 134.

- Which places have the same digits? Which do not? Why?

If time remains, pose additional similar problems using these numbers: 289 and 227.

ACTIVITY

① Sorting Solids

40 MIN GROUPS

For the next few weeks, you're going to be learning about geometry. In the last geometry unit, you identified 2-dimensional shapes (such as rectangles and triangles) and found the perimeter and area of some of these shapes. In this unit you're going to work with 3-dimensional shapes (such as prisms, cylinders, and pyramids) and measurement. You will figure out how many cubes fit in boxes and design your own boxes to hold different arrangements of cubes. First, you're going to do an activity to help you learn about the names and characteristics of 3-D shapes. ❶

Organize the class in as many groups as there are sets of geometric solids and give each group a set. ❷

Let's try to figure out how these wooden shapes are the same and how they are different. Put the shapes into groups so that all the shapes in each group are alike in some way.

Ask students for a few ideas about ways to sort the shapes. Then explain that they will work in their groups to sort the shapes into different categories four or five times. Ask students to try at least one sort using two groups and one using three. Each group of students will keep a recording sheet for their results. Model one way you can sort the solids into two groups.

On a sheet of paper, write the numbers that are on the shapes in each group and circle them to show they go together. Then write how the shapes in each group are the same.

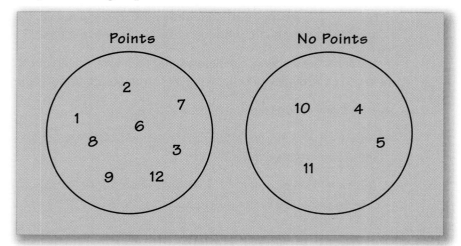

Teaching Note

❶ **Teaching This Unit** Some teachers have found this unit challenging to teach because they have had little opportunity to experience these kinds of problems. Many adults remember geometry as the memorization of proofs and theorems with little time spent handling, observing, and constructing the building blocks of geometry (2-D and 3-D shapes). However, with appropriate experience, everyone can improve his or her ability to visualize—even as an adult. Moreover, many spatial problems that are difficult to visualize are easily solved if you build a concrete model of the situation. If any of the tasks in this unit seem difficult at first reading, try them with concrete materials, just as the students will be doing.

Math Note

❷ **Rectangular Prisms, Boxes, and 3-D Cube Arrays** A geometric *solid* is a shape that has three dimensions—length, width, and height. In mathematics, these shapes are called "solids" whether they are filled or hollow. A rectangular prism is a solid with 6 rectangular faces and edges that are perpendicular to each other. In this unit, students work with various representations of rectangular prisms, such as open boxes and congruent layers of cubes arranged in arrays. Each of these representations forms a solid in the shape of a rectangular prism.

❸ **Teacher Note:** Geometric Solids: Types and Terminology, p. 95

Students will devise numerous methods of sorting the shapes. Many will sort the solids into polyhedra (shapes with only flat sides) and nonpolyhedra (shapes with curved surfaces), describing their categories as "those that roll and those that don't roll." Some students will include octagonal and hexagonal prisms with the figures that roll. Some students might sort the figures into solids with and without points at the top.

Note that the cube and the rectangular prism in this set have similar dimensions and are easily confused. Compare these two carefully yourself and with your students to help them consider the differences.❸

ONGOING ASSESSMENT: Observing Students at Work

Students attend to the components of geometric solids as they sort the set of geometric solids into groups of like shapes.

As students work, look to see what they understand about the attributes of the different shapes.

- **Are they viewing the solids only as wholes and grouping together those whose overall shape seems similar (e.g., these are all tall)?**

- **Are they viewing the shapes functionally, saying that the octagonal and hexagonal prisms are alike because "they roll"?**

- **Are they thinking about how one shape can be transformed into another (e.g., if you take the sides [the flatness] away from these [the octagonal and hexagonal prisms], they will be just like this [the narrow cylinder])?**

- **Are they paying attention to the components of the figures?**
  For example, are they putting together the square pyramid, the cube, and the narrow square prism because "they all have squares"?

As students are working, circulate around the room, asking questions to help you determine what characteristics students are using as they sort.

- How many groups did you make this time?

- How are the shapes in this group the same? How are the shapes in these two groups different?

- Does every shape in this group fit your description? Do any shapes in other groups also fit this description?

DIFFERENTIATION: Supporting the Range of Learners

Intervention If you come upon a group of students having difficulty with the sorting activity, choose one shape from the set of solids and ask the students to describe it.

Are there other shapes in the set that share some of the characteristics you just described? For example, you said that this shape has all flat sides. Can you find other shapes with all flat sides? Are there any solids that don't share this characteristic?

Encourage students who are viewing the shapes only functionally to use other characteristics. Ask questions such as the following:

I noticed that you sorted the solids into shapes that roll and shapes that don't roll. What is it about these shapes that makes them roll? Why can't the shapes in the other group roll?

ELL This is a good opportunity to group English Language Learners with native English speakers. While English Language Learners may be able to see the various characteristics of the solids and be able to sort them, they might not have the vocabulary to discuss the characteristics they used for sorting. Working in a group where they will hear the mathematical terms in context will help with the acquisition of this vocabulary. Students can write and illustrate the new words in picture dictionaries to use as a reference throughout the unit.

DISCUSSION

② Thinking About Sorting Schemes

20 MIN   CLASS

Math Focus Points for Discussion

◆ Distinguishing between polyhedra and nonpolyhedra

◆ Distinguishing between prisms and pyramids

After students have sorted the figures four or five times, ask them to describe some of the categories they used. Guide the discussion by asking the same questions you asked the small groups. Help students focus on the criteria for sorting; that is, on how the shapes in a group are alike and how they are different from the shapes in another group.

If none of the students has sorted the shapes into polyhedra and nonpolyhedra, discuss or model this now. Place the cone, sphere, hemisphere, and both cylinders in one group (nonpolyhedra) and the rest of the shapes in another group (polyhedra).

Professional Development

④ **Dialogue Box:** Talking to Students About Sorting, p. 107

Teaching Note

⑤ **Teaching This Unit** Some of the polyhedra on the homework pages may be difficult to find in the "real world." Also, some of the shapes may be difficult to recognize. For instance, most pencils are hexagonal prisms, but few students will recognize that until it is pointed out. A stop sign is an octagonal prism, but because it is so thin, most students will not recognize it as such. Some still refuse to accept a stop sign as an example of an octagonal prism even when it is explained.

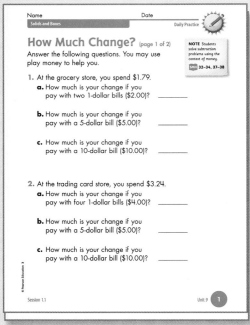

▲ Student Activity Book, pp. 1–2

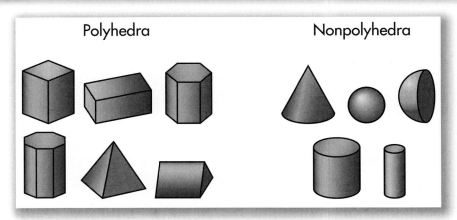

Polyhedra   Nonpolyhedra

How do you think I chose which solids to put into each of these two groups? What do the solids in this group (point to the polyhedra) have in common?

Some students may characterize them as solids that have edges (lines) and faces (flat surfaces). Explain to the students that solids with only flat faces are called polyhedra.

If I had another solid, what would it have to be like for me to place it in the polyhedra group?

Now remove the nonpolyhedra and sort the remaining solids into prisms in one group and the pyramid in the other. If possible, add other pyramids to the set.

How do you think I chose which solids to put into each of these two groups? What do the solids in this group [point to the prisms] have in common?

Students might say:

"Prisms do not have points on top."

"Prisms have tops and bottoms that are the same."

"When prisms are on their bases, the sides are rectangles but the sides of pyramids are triangles."④

SESSION FOLLOW-UP

③ Daily Practice and Homework

 Daily Practice: For ongoing review, have students complete *Student Activity Book* pages 1–2.

 Homework: Ask students to look around their homes for examples of shapes on *Student Activity Book* pages 3–5, and write about any examples they find. They can also look in books and magazines for examples and trace or draw them on a separate sheet of paper. ❺

 Student Math Handbook: Students and families may use *Student Math Handbook* pages 125, 126, 129–130 for reference and review. See pages 115–117 in the back of this unit.

Family Letter: Send home copies of Family Letter (M7–M8).

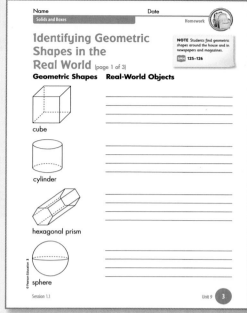

▲ **Student Activity Book, p. 3**

▲ **Student Activity Book, p. 5**

▲ **Student Activity Book, p. 4**

What's My Shape?

Math Focus Points

◆ Describing the components and properties of different classes of solids such as polyhedra (3-D shapes having only flat surfaces, such as prisms and pyramids) and nonpolyhedra (3-D shapes such as cones and cylinders)

Vocabulary

vertex (vertices)

Today's Plan		Materials
ACTIVITY ① Introducing *What's My Shape?*	🕐 20 MIN 👥 CLASS	• Geometric solids; chart paper*
ACTIVIY ② Playing *What's My Shape?*	🕐 40 MIN 👥 GROUPS	• Geometric solids
SESSION FOLLOW-UP ③ Daily Practice		• *Student Activity Book*, p. 7 • *Student Math Handbook*, pp. 127–128

*See *Materials to Prepare*, p. 19.

Ten-Minute Math

Practicing Place Value Write 246 on the board and have students practice saying it to a partner. Ask students:

- How many groups of 10 are in the number? *(24)*
- How many 1s would be left? *(6)*
- If I wanted to break up 246 so that there were some 10s and *16* 1s, how many 10s would there be? *(23)*
- What if I wanted *26* 1s? *(22)*
- What if I wanted *20* 10s? How many ones would there be? *(46)* Does anyone notice a pattern?

If time remains, pose additional similar problems using these numbers: 207 and 191.

ACTIVITY

Introducing *What's My Shape?*

20 MIN   CLASS

This identification game encourages students to make more precise descriptions of geometric solids. Play the game with the whole class for several rounds and then in small groups of 4 to 6 players. Each group needs a set of geometric solids. Set the groups up first and distribute the sets of solids so that students have access to the shapes as you play the demonstration rounds. ❶

To play, one person, known as the Chooser, picks a shape and writes its name on a sheet of paper out of sight of the other students. The other students work as a team to determine what the mystery shape is. They take turns asking yes/no questions that will help them narrow the possibilities and identify the shape. They must decide as a group on the identity of the mystery shape. Students should be encouraged to discuss the possible answers of their questions, making the thinking process an object of discussion.

For the first round, you should be the Chooser. Use this first round to establish the protocol of the game. Encourage students to work cooperatively and prompt them to clarify ambiguous questions. After each question is answered, students will decide together which figures have been eliminated and move those figures aside.

We are going to play a game called What's My Shape? I'm going to be the Chooser. The Chooser picks a mystery shape and writes its name on the sheet of paper. Your job is to work together to figure out what the mystery shape is.

Students asking questions in *What's My Shape?* have five rules to follow. Post the "Rules for Playing *What's My Shape?*" chart that you prepared. Remind students to refer to these rules while they are learning to play the game. ❷

Rules for Playing *What's My Shape?*

1. You must take turns asking questions.

2. You can ask only questions that have a yes/no answer.

3. You cannot ask directly what the shape is (that is, you cannot ask, "Is the shape a sphere? Is it number 7?").

4. You cannot point to a shape.

5. You cannot name an object that looks like the shape (that is, you cannot ask, "Does the shape look like a tepee?").

Differentiation

❶ **English Language Learners** English Language Learners might have initial difficulties understanding the instructions for this game. You can model the game for them in a small group before introducing it to the full class. Include a violation of each rule while playing a sample game in order to emphasize the difference between "good" and "bad" questions. You might also consider different types of groupings for English Language Learners. Some English Language Learners might be more comfortable in an all-English Language Learners group, while others might benefit from listening in on a game before being asked to participate. Encourage English Language Learners to use their picture dictionaries for reference and to participate verbally when they are ready.

Professional Development

❷ **Dialogue Box:** Playing *What's My Shape?*, p. 108

The second time you play as a whole class, select a student to be the Chooser. Model effective types of questions by asking one or two yourself. This can help students learn what attributes they should be thinking about.

What's My Shape? is a fun way for students to learn about the attributes of 3-D shapes.

Does your shape have any square faces?

Does your shape have 8 vertices? Remember, *vertices* is the word mathematicians use for *corners*.

Students might not think of describing a figure by the shape of its faces or by the number of corners, or vertices, it has. However, after you do so, many students will realize that this is a good way to talk about shapes.

You can also make suggestions when a student is unable to think of a question.

Could you think of a question about the corners or edges of the shapes?

ACTIVITY
② Playing *What's My Shape?*

40 MIN GROUPS

As the students play the game in small groups, continue to watch for communication problems. For example, some students will consider all vertices as corners, and others will consider only those on top as corners. Students might interpret questions in different ways. Some students might use *sides* to mean only lateral faces, excluding the tops and bottoms in prisms. To facilitate communication, encourage students to explain the meanings of the terms they use. Continue to model mathematical vocabulary (e.g., *faces* versus *sides* and *vertices* versus *corners*), but do not insist that students use those terms. Over time, many third graders will begin to use the correct terminology.❸

ONGOING ASSESSMENT: Observing Students at Work

Students develop knowledge of the components of various geometric shapes as they ask questions to identify a mystery figure.

- **What attributes are students paying attention to as they ask questions about the mystery figure?** Are they noticing the number and the shape of the faces on each of the geometric solids and asking questions that reflect this?

- **Do their questions demonstrate an understanding of the difference between polyhedra and nonpolyhedra?** Do they ask questions such as, *Does the shape have only flat faces?*

- **Are students accurately determining which figures to eliminate after each question?**

DIFFERENTIATION: Supporting the Range of Learners

Intervention Some students may be having difficulty moving beyond the description of the shape as a whole and attending to its component parts. Some possibilities for helping these students include the following:

- **Joining the game for a couple of turns to model some questions for them**

- **Selecting a solid from the set and asking questions about the number of faces, edges, and corners and about the shape of the faces to encourage students to attend to these components**

SESSION FOLLOW-UP

Daily Practice

 Daily Practice: For reinforcement of this unit's content, have students complete *Student Activity Book* page 7.

Student Math Handbook: Students and families may use *Student Math Handbook* pages 127–128 for reference and review. See pages 115–117 in the back of this unit.

Professional Development

❸ **Dialogue Box:** Building Common Vocabulary, p. 109

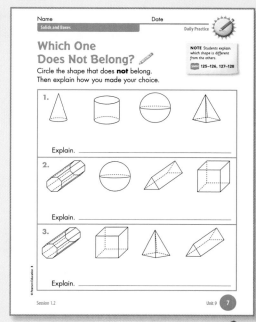

Name _____ Date _____
Solids and Boxes   Daily Practice

Which One Does Not Belong?
Circle the shape that does **not** belong. Then explain how you made your choice.

NOTE Students explain which shape is different from the others.
125–126, 127–128

1.

Explain. _____

2.

Explain. _____

3.

Explain. _____

Session 1.2   Unit 9 7

▲ **Student Activity Book, p. 7**

Building Polyhedra from Pictures or Models

Math Focus Points

◆ Distinguishing between polyhedra and nonpolyhedra

◆ Identifying the components of polyhedra (faces, edges, and vertices) and how they come together to form the whole

◆ Visualizing and building polyhedra by using knowledge of their components (faces, edges, and vertices) and how they come together to form the whole

Today's Plan		Materials
ACTIVITY ❶ **Building Polyhedra**	🕐 40 MIN 👥 PAIRS	• *Student Activity Book*, p. 8 • Building kits*; geometric solids (from Session 1.1)
DISCUSSION ❷ **Looking at What We Built**	🕐 20 MIN 👥 CLASS	• Geometric solids; student-built polyhedra
SESSION FOLLOW-UP ❸ **Daily Practice and Homework**		• *Student Activity Book*, pp. 9–11 • *Student Math Handbook*, pp. 125–126, 127–128 • M9–M10, Family Letter*

*See *Materials to Prepare*, p. 19.

Ten-Minute Math

Practicing Place Value Say "two hundred fifty-three," and ask students to write the number. Make sure all students can read, write, and say this number correctly. Ask students to solve these problems mentally, if possible:

- What is: $253 + 30$? $253 + 40$? $253 - 40$? $253 + 100$? $253 - 100$? $253 + 300$?

Write each answer on the board. Ask students to compare each sum or difference with 253.

- Which places have the same digits? Which do not? Why?

If time remains, pose additional similar problems using these numbers: 291 and 305.

ACTIVITY

1 Building Polyhedra

40 MIN   PAIRS

Before you ask students to build polyhedra, it is a good idea for you to make some yourself. This will give you an idea of what may arise for students as they work on this activity.

Distribute a Building kit to each pair of students. Students will be familiar with these kits from the work they did with building polygons in *Perimeter, Angles, and Area* (Unit 4). To remind students of how to use the Building kits, demonstrate by building a polygon (such as a square or triangle) with the sticks and connectors. Distribute sets of geometric solids for two or three student pairs to share. Explain to students that they will use these kits to build models of the 3-dimensional figures pictured on *Student Activity Book* page 8.

Which figures on the sheet can you build with the sticks and connectors? You may not bend the sticks.

Students should recognize that because the sticks cannot be bent, only the polyhedra can be built with the sticks and connectors.

If you can't figure out how to build a figure by looking at its picture, you can look at the wooden model to help you. If you can build a figure, write how many edges and corners it has next to its picture on *Student Activity Book* page 8. If you cannot build a figure with your kit, write *No* beside the picture. ❶

✔ ONGOING ASSESSMENT: Observing Students at Work

Students develop understanding of the structure of polyhedra and the spatial relationships among their components by building polyhedra while looking at pictures or models.

- **Do students quickly distinguish between the figures that they can build (polyhedra) and those that they cannot (nonpolyhedra)?**

- **Are they accurately counting the edges and vertices or are they undercounting some components or counting the same components more than once?**

- **Are students able to successfully build the polyhedra pictured on *Student Activity Book* page 8?**

Math Note

❶ **Student Difficulties Counting Components** At this grade level, counting the parts of a polyhedron can be a difficult task. Some students make the common mistake of counting edges more than once, focusing on the shape of each face instead of the figure as a whole. For example, when counting the edges of a cube, students may attend to the 6 squares that make up the faces and count the 4 sides of each square as an edge of the cube. As a result, they may say that a cube has 24 edges (6×4) instead of 12, failing to recognize that some of the sides of the squares are shared by more than one face.

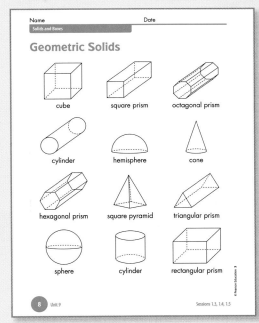

▲ Student Activity Book, p. 8

DIFFERENTIATION: Supporting the Range of Learners

Intervention If students are having difficulty counting the parts of the polyhedra, demonstrate organized thinking during counting. For a rectangular prism, for example, you might point to each part as you say,

I counted 4 edges on the bottom, 4 more on the top, and 2 more on the two sides.

This will help students keep track of what has already been counted and what remains to be counted.

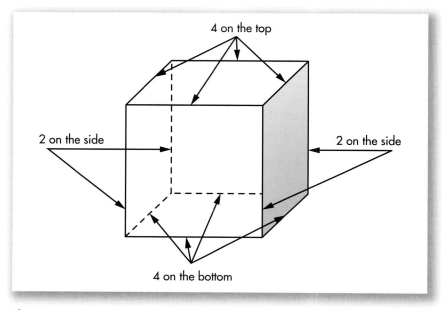

4 on the top

2 on the side   2 on the side

4 on the bottom

If many students are having this problem, you can call the class together briefly and do this demonstration for the whole class.

20 MIN   CLASS

DISCUSSION
Looking at What We Built

Math Focus Points for Discussion

◆ Distinguishing between polyhedra and nonpolyhedra

◆ Visualizing and building polyhedra by using knowledge of their components (faces, edges, and vertices) and how they come together to form the whole

About 20 minutes before the end of the session, call the students together to discuss the polyhedra they constructed.

Which figures could you build with your sticks and connectors? How are these figures different from the ones you could not build?

Students should notice that the figures they could build are the ones which have all flat sides and that the ones they could not build have curved sides. After students have made this distinction, remind them that the figures with "only flat sides" are called polyhedra. The word polyhedron (plural, *polyhedra*) means "having many faces."

Ask students about their strategies for counting the faces of different polyhedra. Have volunteers demonstrate how they counted on an actual solid and on a shape they constructed.

Of the geometric solids you built, which has the most faces? Which has the least? Why do you think that the octagonal prism has more faces than the triangular prism?

Students may respond by saying that an octagonal prism has more faces than a triangular prism because an octagon has more sides than a triangle, recognizing a connection between the number of faces on a polyhedron and the type of polyhedron it is. In other words, the more sides the figures that form the top and bottom of the prism have, the more faces the prism has. Consequently, an octagonal prism has more faces than a triangular prism.❷

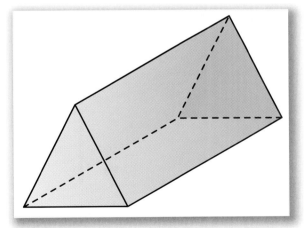

During the discussion, encourage students to use the geometric names that appear on *Student Activity Book* page 8, but allow them to use more informal names such as "box." Students are not expected to memorize the geometric names. However, with repeated exposure to these names, many students will begin to use them.

Math Note

❷ **Determining the Number of Faces of a Prism**
As you do this work with your students, you may have noticed that the number of faces on any prism is equal to the number of sides on the shape that make up the "top and bottom" plus 2. Consequently, a triangular prism has 5 faces since a triangle has 3 sides (see below); a rectangular prism has 6 faces since a rectangle has 4 sides; an octagonal prism has 10 faces since an octagon has 8 sides, and so on. Do not expect students to fully understand this relationship at this time, as it is a complicated idea for third graders to grasp. It is sufficient for them to simply notice that a triangular prism has the fewest faces and an octagonal prism has the most faces among the polyhedra in the set and to begin to think about why this is so.

Name _____ Date _____
Solids and Boxes   Daily Practice

Our Collections (page 1 of 2)

For each problem, write an equation that
represents the problem, solve the problem,
and show your solution.

NOTE Students solve addition
and subtraction problems in a
story problem context.
DMR 20–24, 32–35

1. Deondra collects coins. She had 385 coins in
   her collection. On her birthday her uncle gave
   her 125 more coins to add to her collection.
   How many coins does Deondra have now?

2. Oscar collects comic books. He has 462
   superhero comic books and 394 cartoon
   comic books. How many comic books does
   he have altogether?

Session 1.3   Unit 9   9

▲ Student Activity Book, p. 9

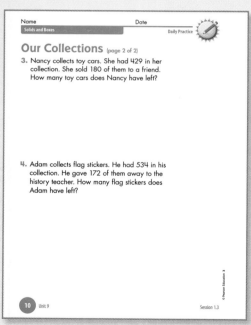

Name _____ Date _____
Solids and Boxes   Daily Practice

Our Collections (page 2 of 2)

3. Nancy collects toy cars. She had 429 in her
   collection. She sold 180 of them to a friend.
   How many toy cars does Nancy have left?

4. Adam collects flag stickers. He had 534 in his
   collection. He gave 172 of them away to the
   history teacher. How many flag stickers does
   Adam have left?

10 Unit 9   Session 1.3

▲ Student Activity Book, p. 10

SESSION FOLLOW-UP

③ Daily Practice and Homework

Daily Practice: For ongoing review, have students complete
Student Activity Book pages 9–10.

Homework: Students solve addition problems with 3-digit
numbers on *Student Activity Book* page 11.

Student Math Handbook: Students and families may use
Student Math Handbook pages 125–126, 127–128 for reference
and review. See pages 115–117 in the back of this unit.

Family Letter: Send home copies of Family Letter (M9–M10).

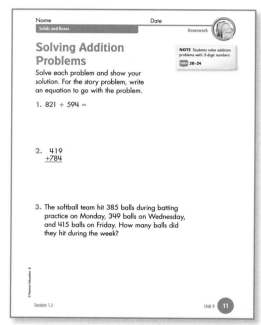

Name _____ Date _____
Solids and Boxes   Homework

Solving Addition Problems

Solve each problem and show your
solution. For the story problem, write
an equation to go with the problem.

NOTE Students solve addition
problems with 3-digit numbers.
DMR 20–24

1. 821 + 594 =

2.   419
   +784

3. The softball team hit 385 balls during batting
   practice on Monday, 349 balls on Wednesday,
   and 415 balls on Friday. How many balls did
   they hit during the week?

Session 1.3   Unit 9   11

▲ Student Activity Book, p. 11

Assessment: Building Polyhedra from Descriptions—Day 1

Math Focus Points

◆ Identifying the components of polyhedra (faces, edges, and vertices) and how they come together to form the whole

◆ Visualizing and building polyhedra by using knowledge of their components (faces, edges, and vertices) and how they come together to form the whole

Vocabulary

polyhedron	figure
polyhedra	

Today's Plan		Materials
1 ACTIVITY **Introducing Building from Descriptions**	10 MIN INDIVIDUALS CLASS	• T102* • *Student Activity Book*, p. 8 • Geometric solids (from Session 1.1; Building kits (from Session 1.3)
2 ASSESSMENT ACTIVITY **Building Polyhedra from Descriptions—Day 1**	✓ 30 MIN INDIVIDUALS	• *Student Activity Book*, pp. 8, 13 • M12* ☑ • Geometric solids (from Session 1.1; Building kits
3 DISCUSSION **What Solid Did You Build?**	20 MIN CLASS	• T102 • Student-built polyhedra
4 SESSION FOLLOW-UP **Daily Practice**		• *Student Activity Book*, p. 14 • *Student Math Handbook*, pp. 127–128

*See *Materials to Prepare,* p. 21.

Ten-Minute Math

Practicing Place Value Say "four hundred eight," and ask students to write the number. Make sure all students can read, write, and say this number correctly. Ask students to solve these problems mentally, if possible:

• What is: 408 − 30?   408 + 30?   408 + 50?   408 − 300?   408 + 300?

Differentiation

❶ English Language Learners English Language Learners might need to hear the descriptions read aloud more than once in order to grasp their meaning. You might have English Language Learners work in pairs on this activity so they can support each other's understanding of the task. Since students will be asked to write their own descriptions and comparisons of shapes on the assessment, you might model the writing by recording the answers students give during the post-activity class discussion. If an English Language Learner has great difficulty expressing ideas in English, you can ask the student to point out key characteristics while you provide the necessary language. *That's right. Both of the polyhedra have flat edges.*

Solids and Boxes

Building Polyhedra

1. Build a polyhedron that has exactly 6 square faces.

2. Build a polyhedron that has exactly 1 square face and 4 triangular faces.

3. Build a polyhedron that has exactly 3 rectangular faces and 2 triangular faces.

4. Build a polyhedron that has exactly 8 corners and 6 faces.

5. Build a polyhedron that has exactly 5 corners and 5 faces.

6. How many differently-shaped polyhedra can you make that have exactly 12 edges?

Optional

Make a polyhedron that has exactly 6 edges and 4 triangular faces.

T102

▲ **Transparencies, T102**

ACTIVITY

1 Introducing Building from Descriptions

10 MIN INDIVIDUALS CLASS

Show the transparency Building Polyhedra (T102).

In our last math class, you built polyhedra by looking at pictures. Today and tomorrow, you're going to build **polyhedra** by listening to or reading descriptions. After we read a description of a **polyhedron**, try to picture in your mind what it looks like. Then build it.

Read the first problem aloud. Let students know that they can look at the pictures of solids on *Student Activity Book* page 8 or at the wooden models if they are having difficulty picturing the form in their minds. They can then count the edges or examine faces of real or pictured objects instead of relying on visual imagery.

When students have completed the first problem, have them compare figures.

Hold up the first **figure** you built and look at the figures of your classmates. How are the figures the same? How are they different?

[Point out two different figures built for Problem 1.] These two don't look the same. Are they both correct? How do you know? How did you figure out how to build this polyhedron?❶

Building geometric solids makes it easier for students to understand their attributes.

ASSESSMENT ACTIVITY

 Building Polyhedra from Descriptions—Day 1

30 MIN INDIVIDUALS

Students build the polyhedra described in Problems 2 and 3 on *Student Activity Book* page 13. Because students are not building all of the polyhedra on the *Student Activity Book* page in this session, they will not need to disassemble one polyhedron before building the next. Explain that they will complete the problems in the next session.

During this session and the next, observe students as they are building the polyhedra. Use Assessment Checklist: Building Polyhedra from Descriptions (M12) to keep track of how individual students are doing on this task.

Plan to observe some students in this session and the rest in Session 1.5. Keep in mind that you may need to observe some students a second time in that session. This will allow you to assess whether students you observe having difficulty in this session are able to understand the process after participating in the discussion at the end of this session.

This observed assessment addresses the first benchmark for this unit:

1. Identify and compare attributes of three-dimensional solids.

Students' solution strategies will vary. Some build the parts of the figure described (e.g., number and shapes of faces, edges, and vertices) and then try to fit the parts together. Others look for a picture or wooden model that fits the description and then build a figure like it. Still others simply visualize the solution and then build it from their visual image. As students work, watch for the use of each of these strategies. You can identify certain students whose strategies you wish to highlight in the discussion that follows.

ONGOING ASSESSMENT: Observing Students at Work

Students demonstrate their understanding of the components of geometric solids and how these components form the whole by building polyhedra from written and verbal directions.

- **Are students able to correctly build all or most of the polyhedra?**
- **Do they need to use the reference sheet or wooden models in order to do so?**

Math Note

❶ **Solutions for Building Polyhedra** Solutions for problems 2–3 on Building Polyhedra (T102): Problem 2, any square pyramid; and Problem 3, any triangular prism.

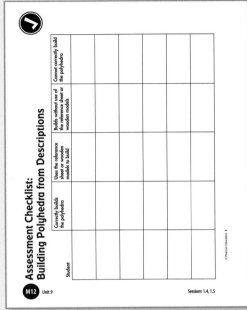

▲ **Resource Masters, M12**

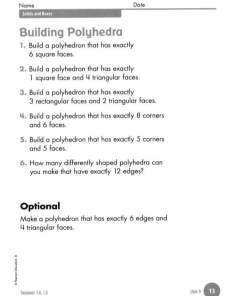

Name _____ Date _____
Solids and Boxes

Building Polyhedra

1. Build a polyhedron that has exactly 6 square faces.
2. Build a polyhedron that has exactly 1 square face and 4 triangular faces.
3. Build a polyhedron that has exactly 3 rectangular faces and 2 triangular faces.
4. Build a polyhedron that has exactly 8 corners and 6 faces.
5. Build a polyhedron that has exactly 5 corners and 5 faces.
6. How many differently shaped polyhedra can you make that have exactly 12 edges?

Optional
Make a polyhedron that has exactly 6 edges and 4 triangular faces.

Sessions 1.4, 1.5   Unit 9 13

▲ **Student Activity Book, p. 13**

- **Can they complete the problems without looking at the reference sheet or the wooden models?**

- **Can students identify properties of polyhedra?** Can they identify a face, a vertex, and an edge?

Those students using pictures or models to help them build the polyhedra have developed practical knowledge of the concept of polyhedra and their components. Students who are able to build without referring to pictures or models have developed not only excellent visualization skills but also a more sophisticated understanding of polyhedra and the relationships among their components.

DIFFERENTIATION: Supporting the Range of Learners

Intervention Some students may not be able to build the polyhedra from verbal or written descriptions even with the pictures on *Student Activity Book* page 8 and the wooden models to refer to. Help these students with a review of *polyhedra, vertices, faces,* and *edges* to make sure that they understand each part. In addition, some students may need more experience with building polyhedra directly from the wooden models or from diagrams.

Extension Students who finish this task before the 30 minutes are up can use other sticks from the kit to build a second polyhedron for each problem.

DISCUSSION

20 MIN   CLASS

3 What Solid Did You Build?

Math Focus Points for Discussion

◆ Visualizing and building polyhedra by using knowledge of their components (faces, edges, and vertices) and how they come together to form the whole

Call students together for a full-class discussion. Display the transparency Building Polyhedra (T102), and direct their attention to Problem 2 ("Build a polyhedron that has exactly 1 square face and 4 triangular faces."). Ask students to hold up the polyhedra they built for this problem to compare theirs with their classmates'.

How are these figures the same? How are they different? These two don't look the same. Are they both correct? How do you know?

Because students may have used different-sized sticks to construct the polyhedron described in Problem 2, they may comment on the fact that the figures constructed are not all the same size, as is shown in the figure below.

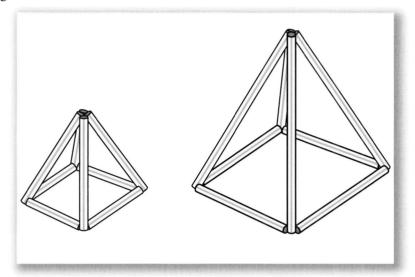

▲ **Student Activity Book, p. 14**

Make sure that students also recognize what is alike about the figures (same number of vertices, edges, faces, and so on).

How did you figure out how to build this polyhedron? Did you have a picture in your mind of what the polyhedron would look like before you built it? Did you look first at the geometric solids to find one that fit the description?

Use the observations you made as students were working to ensure that strategies are shared between students who needed to look at the solids before building their solid and students who were able to visualize the polyhedron first. If students have not already done so, ask them to name the polyhedron built from the description in Problem 2.

If time allows, follow the same procedure with Problem 3.

SESSION FOLLOW-UP

Daily Practice

 Daily Practice: For ongoing review, have students complete *Student Activity Book* page 14.

 Student Math Handbook: Students and families may use *Student Math Handbook* pages 127–128 for reference and review. See pages 115–117 in the back of this unit.

Building Polyhedra from Descriptions—Day 2

Math Focus Points

◆ Identifying the components of polyhedra (faces, edges, and vertices) and how they come together to form the whole

◆ Visualizing and building polyhedra by using knowledge of their components (faces, edges, and vertices) and how they come together to form the whole

Vocabulary
rectangular prism
pyramid

Today's Plan		Materials
① ASSESSMENT ACTIVITY **Building Polyhedra from Descriptions—Day 2**	40 MIN INDIVIDUALS	• *Student Activity Book,* pp. 8, 13 • M12 ☑ • Geometric solids (from Session 1.1); Building kits (from Session 1.3)
② DISCUSSION **Discussing Problem 6**	20 MIN CLASS	• T102 ; or *Student Activity Book,* p. 13 • Student-built polyhedra for Problem 6 • Hexagonal pyramid (if needed)*
③ SESSION FOLLOW-UP **Daily Practice and Homework**		• *Student Activity Book,* p. 15 • M13*; M14* • *Student Math Handbook,* pp. 127–128, 129–130

*See *Materials to Prepare,* p. 21.

Ten-Minute Math
Practicing Place Value Write 654 on the board and have students practice *saying* it to a partner. Ask students:

• How many groups of 10 are in the number? *(65)* How many ones are left? *(4)* If I wanted to break up 654 so that there were some tens and *54* ones, how many tens would there be? *(60)* What if I wanted *34* ones? *(62)* What if I wanted *59* tens? How many ones would there be? *(64)* Does anyone notice a pattern?

If time remains, pose additional similar problems using these numbers: 677 and 703.

ASSESSMENT ACTIVITY

Assessment: Building Polyhedra from Descriptions—Day 2

40 MIN INDIVIDUALS

During this session, students work on Problems 4–6 of *Student Activity Book* page 13. Use Assessment Checklist: Building Polyhedra from Descriptions (M12) to observe the remaining students and any whom you observed having difficulty with the task in Session 1.4. Focus your observations on the work students are doing on Problems 4 and 5 because Problem 6 has a different emphasis.

Let students know that to answer Problem 6 on *Student Activity Book* page 13, they should name the figures they make, tell how many vertices and edges the figures have, tell the lengths of the sticks used, and describe the shapes of the faces. The emphasis of this activity is on using imagery to generate ideas, not exhausting all the possibilities.

To prepare for the discussion of Problem 6 at the end of the session, look for a student who has built a rectangular prism that is not a cube, a student who has built a cube, and (if possible) a student who has built a pyramid. Ask these students to be prepared to show and discuss their examples.❶

ONGOING ASSESSMENT: Observing Students at Work

Students demonstrate their understanding of the components of geometric solids and how these components form the whole by building polyhedra from written descriptions.

- **Are students able to correctly build all or most of the polyhedra?**

- **Do they need to use the reference sheet or wooden models to build the polyhedra?** Can they complete the problems without looking at the reference sheet or the wooden models?

- **What figures are students building for Problem 6?** Are they building different sizes of rectangular prisms, including cubes? Do they recognize that there is a pyramid that can be built that meets this description?

Math Note

❶ **Solutions for Building Polyhedra** Solutions for the last three problems and the optional problem on the transparency Building Polyhedra (T102) are as follows: Problem 4, any rectangular prism, including a cube; Problem 5, any square pyramid; Problem 6, any rectangular prism or hexagonal pyramid. There are other less familiar possibilities (e.g., any prism with a four-sided base such as a trapezoid, rhombus, or parallelogram). The solution for the Optional problem is any triangular pyramid.

DIFFERENTIATION: Supporting the Range of Learners

Intervention As students are working, encourage those who are successfully building polyhedra, but need to look first at the geometric solids, to try to create a picture in their minds of what the polyhedron will look like before building it. Do not, however, require that they do so because some students will not develop the ability to visualize the figure without more building experience.

Extension Students working on Problem 6 by building rectangular prisms (including cubes) of different sizes may not have thought to consider whether a pyramid could fit this description. Ask them to think about the number of edges on a triangular pyramid and on a square pyramid and to think about whether that information could help them come up with a pyramid with 12 edges. They may recognize that the number of edges on a pyramid is equal to twice the number of sides of its base.

DISCUSSION

② Discussing Problem 6

20 MIN CLASS

Math Focus Points for Discussion

◆ Visualizing and building polyhedra by using knowledge of their components (faces, edges, and vertices) and how they come together to form the whole

Direct the class's attention to Problem 6 on the transparency Building Polyhedra (T102) or *Student Activity Book* page 13. Ask students who built the rectangular prism, the cube, and the hexagonal pyramid to hold up their polyhedra for their classmates to see. If no students have built a hexagonal pyramid, hold one up that you prepared before the discussion.

These are three of the polyhedra that students built to match the description in Problem 6. What kind of polyhedron is each one? Can they all be correct answers? How do you know?

Students are likely to count the edges of each of the three figures to confirm that each one has 12 edges. After all of the students are convinced that each figure fits the description in Problem 6, hold up the cube and ask these questions:

What would we need to add to the description in Problem 6 so that the cube would be the only polyhedron that would work? What would we need to add for the pyramid?

Give students some time to work on answering each of these questions. Some students will be able to visualize the differences between these solids, but others will need to look at the cube and pyramid to examine the components that distinguish them from each other.

After a few minutes, call the class back together to share what students have determined. Listen for students' understanding that adding 6 square faces to the description would describe only the cube and no other rectangular prisms or the hexagonal pyramid.

[Bridget] thinks that adding 6 square faces to the description would describe only the cube. Do you agree with her? Why?

Students might say:

 "I agree. A lot of the shapes have 12 edges, but the cube is the only one that has 6 square faces."

 "I agree, too. The square prism has 12 edges, but it only has 2 square faces. The other faces are rectangles, but they're not squares because they have 2 short and 2 long sides. A square has to have all sides the same."

Similarly, adding one hexagonal face or one hexagonal face and 6 triangular faces to the description would limit the possible answers to the hexagonal pyramid.

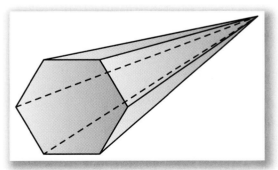

SESSION FOLLOW-UP

③ Daily Practice and Homework

 Daily Practice: For ongoing review, have students complete *Student Activity Book* page 15.

 Homework: Students choose a "secret" polyhedron to describe from the figures on Geometric Solids (M13), and write a description on *What's My Shape?* (M14). Students write the name of the polyhedron on the back of this page. When students bring their homework in the next day, they may trade descriptions and try to guess a polyhedron that matches that description.

 Student Math Handbook: Students and families may use *Student Math Handbook* pages 127–128, 129–130 for reference and review. See pages 115–117 in the back of this unit.

▲ Student Activity Book, p. 15

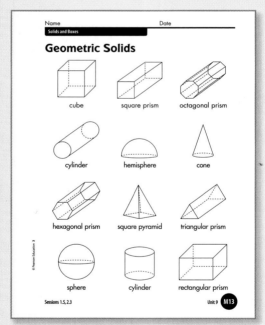

▲ Resource Masters, M13

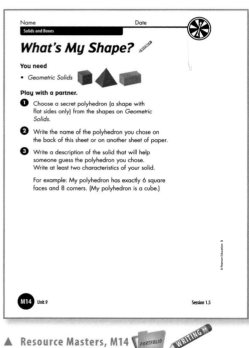

▲ Resource Masters, M14

INVESTIGATION 2

Mathematical Emphasis

Features of Shape Translating between 2-dimensional and 3-dimensional shapes

Math Focus Points

◆ Determining the number and shapes of the faces of cubes and other rectangular prisms and how they come together to form the whole

◆ Designing patterns that make open boxes for a cube

◆ Designing patterns that make open boxes for 2-cube rectangular prisms

◆ Determining the number and shapes of the faces of a triangular pyramid and how they come together to form the whole

◆ Designing patterns that make nets for triangular pyramids

Making Boxes

SESSION 2.1 p. 50	Student Activity Book	Student Math Handbook	Professional Development: Read Ahead of Time	
Making Boxes for a Cube Students determine whether given patterns will make open boxes to hold 1 cube. They design their own open-box patterns.	16–17	131	• **Dialogue Box:** Patterns for Cubes, p. 110	
SESSION 2.2 p. 55				
Patterns for 2-Cube Boxes Students discuss their patterns for 1-cube boxes and explain why these patterns contain 5 squares. They develop their skills translating between 2-D and 3-D shapes as they design open-box patterns to hold 2 cubes.	19	131	• **Dialogue Box:** Making Patterns for the 2-Cube Solid, p. 112	
SESSION 2.3 p. 59				
Patterns for Triangular Pyramids Students discuss the patterns they made for 2-cube rectangular prisms and consider why these boxes must be composed of 8 or 9 squares. They develop their skills translating between 2-D and 3-D shapes as they design closed boxes to hold triangular pyramids.	20–22	131		

More or Less?

- **No materials needed**

Materials to Gather	Materials to Prepare
• **T103, Patterns For Cube Boxes** 🖨 • **Cubes** (1 per student) • **Construction paper** (1 sheet per student) • **Tape** (1 roll per pair) • **Scissors** (1 per student or pair)	• **M15, Patterns For Cube Boxes** Make copies. (1 per student) • **M16, One-Inch Grid Paper** Make copies. (4 per student, plus extras) • **Sample box** Prepare a 1-cube open box from the flat pattern shown on p. 52. Fold and tape the pattern to make the box. • **Chart paper** Prepare a poster titled "Open-Box Pattern Rules" with the rules to make an open-box pattern. See p. 54.
• **Student-made patterns for 1-cube boxes** (from Session 2.1) • **Poster: "Open-Box Pattern Rules"** (from Session 2.1) • **Scissors** (1 per student or pair) • **Chart paper** (optional) • **Cubes** (2 per student or pair)	• **M16, One-Inch Grid Paper** Make copies. (8 per pair; 4 per student; plus extras)
• **M13, Geometric Solids** (from Session 1.5; optional) • **Student-made patterns for 2-cube boxes** (from Session 2.2) • **Chart paper** (optional) • **Scissors** (1 per student or pair) • **Geometric solids** (optional)	• **M17, Triangle Paper** Make copies. (2 per pair plus extras)

🖨 Overhead Transparency

Making Boxes for a Cube

Math Focus Points

◆ Determining the number and shapes of the faces of cubes and other rectangular prisms and how they come together to form the whole

◆ Designing patterns that make open boxes for a cube

Today's Plan		Materials
ACTIVITY **①** **Open Boxes for a Cube**	15 MIN INDIVIDUALS	• Cubes; sample box (optional)*; construction paper; scissors; tape
DISCUSSION **②** **Cube Patterns**	25 MIN CLASS	• M15*; T103 • Scissors; student-made cube box (from Activity 1)
ACTIVITY **③** **More Cube Patterns**	20 MIN PAIRS	• M16* • Chart paper*; scissors
SESSION FOLLOW-UP **④** **Daily Practice and Homework**		• *Student Activity Book,* pp. 16–17 • *Student Math Handbook,* p. 131

*See *Materials to Prepare,* p. 49.

Ten-Minute Math

More or Less? Write the problem 200 + 356 + 472 on the board. Students estimate the sum and decide if it is more or less than 1,000. Select students to share their strategies. Ask:

• What did you pay attention to when you looked at these numbers? What numbers did you add first? Did you use combinations that you know equal 100 or 1,000 to help you?

If time remains, pose additional similar problems such as: 419 + 585.

ACTIVITY
1 Open Boxes for a Cube

15 MIN   INDIVIDUALS

Show students a cube.

Let's imagine that we are box designers working for a box company. For our first project, we must use paper, scissors, and tape to make a box in which this cube fits perfectly. The box should completely cover all but one side of the cube so that we can get the cube in and out easily. No parts of the box should overlap because we are trying to conserve paper. ❶

If students do not understand the task, you can briefly show them an open box that you have made [and kept out of sight] in which the cube fits.

Distribute a cube and one piece of construction paper to each student and explain that they will each be making an open box to hold the cube.

Making a box for a cube is not a simple task for students. There is likely to be a range in how they approach this task.

- Some students will wrap the cube as if wrapping a package. These students may fail to see the box as being made up of squares.

- Others trace the square faces of the cubes on a piece of paper in a seemingly random fashion, cut out their squares, place them on the cube and tape them together. These students see the box as being made up of squares but do not see the squares as connected.

- Other students try to make a pattern of squares that will fold to make the box. If the pattern does not work when they try to fold it, they may start over, or they may cut apart their squares and tape them together in a different arrangement.

- Some students will immediately be able to visualize how the square faces should fit together and will make one of the standard patterns for a cube.

ONGOING ASSESSMENT: Observing Students at Work

Students develop their understanding of the components of a cube by making boxes without tops for holding one cube.

- **What strategies are students using to make their boxes?**

- **Do their strategies indicate an understanding that the box must be composed of 5 squares (because the cube has 6 square faces) that fold to create the edges of the cube?**

Math Note

❶ **Making an Open Box with Unmarked Paper** Using unmarked paper encourages students to focus on the components of a cube (e.g., the fact that a cube is composed of 6 square faces that come together at the edges) before they are given paper that shows that square structure.

Math Notes

② **Cubes Are Rectangular Prisms** In *Perimeter, Angles, and Area* (Unit 4), students learned that a *square* is a particular kind of *rectangle,* one in which all sides are equal. Similarly, a *cube* is a particular kind of *rectangular prism,* one in which all faces are squares.

③ **Defining a "Pattern"** In this unit, the word *pattern* is used to describe the way something is designed or used as a model for construction. Because this definition differs from how *pattern* is defined in previous work that students have done, such as *Stories, Tables, and Graphs* (Unit 6) and when looking for skip-counting patterns in *Equal Groups* (Unit 5) explain this difference to students. Use examples such as dressmaking and model building patterns to illustrate the different uses of this word.

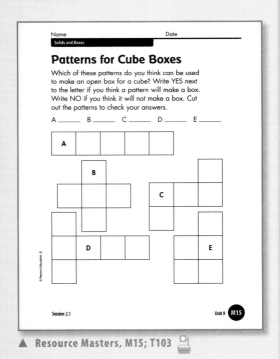

Name _____ Date _____
Solids and Boxes

Patterns for Cube Boxes

Which of these patterns do you think can be used to make an open box for a cube? Write YES next to the letter if you think a pattern will make a box. Write NO if you think it will not make a box. Cut out the patterns to check your answers.

A _____ B _____ C _____ D _____ E _____

Session 2.1   Unit 9 **M15**

▲ **Resource Masters, M15; T103**

DIFFERENTIATION: Supporting the Range of Learners

Intervention If some students do not have the manual dexterity to work with inch cubes, you could let them use larger ones, such as those from the set of geometric solids.

DISCUSSION

② Cube Patterns

25 MIN   CLASS

Math Focus Points for Discussion

◆ Determining the number and shapes of the faces of cubes and other rectangular prisms and how they come together to form the whole②

◆ Designing patterns that make open boxes for a cube

After all of the students have completed their boxes, have a few students who used different strategies show their boxes and explain how they made them. As students share, help them articulate what strategies they used as they worked on this task.

Philip, you said that you traced the faces of the cube to make your box. What did you notice about the cube as you did this? How many square faces did you need to make the box?

Jane, you thought about making a pattern that you could fold. What shapes did you use in your pattern? How did you decide the shapes to use?

Next, hold up the box that you made, and disassemble it to show what it looks like flat. Cut it along the four edges that are perpendicular to the bottom so that it looks like this:

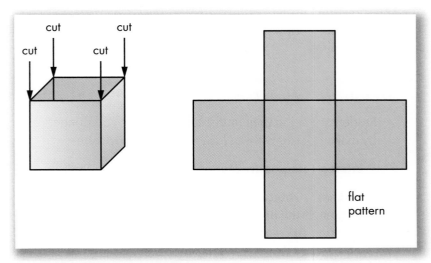

flat pattern

We call this flat piece of paper a pattern for an open box to hold one cube. As you can see, it folds up to make a box without a top. What do you notice about this pattern? What are the shapes of its faces when it's folded? Why is it made from squares? ❸

As students respond, listen for indications that they notice that the sides of the boxes match the faces of the cubes and that the faces of the cubes are squares.

Direct students' attention to Patterns for Cube Boxes (M15).

Talk with your partners about which of these patterns you think will fold to make an open cube box. Talk together about why you think a pattern will or won't make an open box. Then write *yes* next to the letter of each pattern that you think will make an open cube box and *no* next to the letter of each pattern that you think will not. You can use your cubes to help you decide.

After students have made their decisions, instruct them to cut out the patterns to see whether their decisions were correct. Then call the class back together. Use the transparency of Patterns for Cube Boxes (T103) to help focus the discussion.

Which patterns did you think would make an open box for a cube? How did you make your decisions? . . . Which patterns actually made an open box for a cube? Which patterns didn't work? Can you explain why?

For each pattern that did not work, ask students to explain the reason. ❹

---

❸ ACTIVITY
More Cube Patterns

20 MIN · PAIRS

Each pair of students needs 4 copies of One-Inch Grid Paper (M16) for this activity. Have extras available.

Post the "Open-Box Pattern Rules" poster you prepared and explain the rules to the class.

Your next task as box designers is to find more patterns for open boxes that will fit one cube. You will use grid paper to make your patterns, and each pattern must follow three rules. ❺

Professional Development

❹ **Dialogue Box:** Patterns for Cubes, p. 110

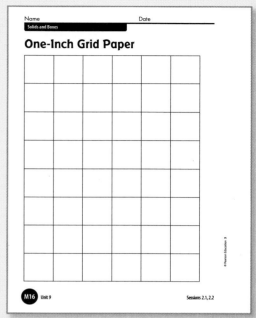

▲ **Resource Masters, M16**

Teaching Note

❺ **Rules for Box Patterns** These rules are designed to help students develop understanding of the components of a cube: number and shape of faces, edges, and so on, and to see how these components come together to form the whole. Using a single sheet of paper necessitates that students consider how the square faces of the cube are connected to one another. Having no overlapping sides allows students to investigate the relationship between the squares in the pattern and the shape and number of faces on the cube.

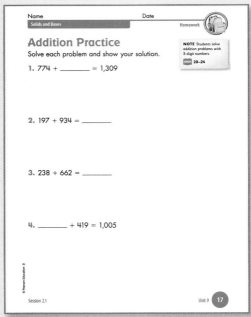

▲ Student Activity Book, p. 16

▲ Student Activity Book, p. 17

Open-Box Pattern Rules

- It must be made from a single sheet of paper.

- It can be folded only along the edges of the squares.

- No sides can overlap.

Tell students that their job today is to design box *patterns,* not to actually put the boxes together. As students cut out the patterns, they fold them around cubes to test their ideas, but they do not tape the patterns. Students discuss their patterns and their strategies for making them at the start of the next math session.

As students are working, you may notice that many of them will not reflect on their errors but instead will start over repeatedly. If a student's pattern fails to make an open box, ask that student how the pattern could be changed to make it work.

I notice that your box doesn't have an open top. What can you do to the pattern to make it work? Can you change it in some way?

ONGOING ASSESSMENT: Observing Students at Work

Students develop and use visualization and spatial reasoning skills as they design patterns for open boxes to hold one cube.

- **Do the students recognize that an open box pattern for a cube must consist of 5 squares because the cube has 6 square faces?**

- **If a student makes a pattern that does not work, does he or she consider why it is not working or simply begin again?**

SESSION FOLLOW-UP
Daily Practice and Homework

 Daily Practice: For ongoing review, have students complete *Student Activity Book* page 16.

 Homework: Students solve addition problems with 3-digit numbers on *Student Activity Book* page 17.

Student Math Handbook: Students and families may use *Student Math Handbook* page 131 for reference and review. See pages 115–117 in the back of this unit.

Patterns for 2-Cube Boxes

Math Focus Points

◈ Designing patterns that make open boxes for 2-cube rectangular prisms

◈ Determining the number and shapes of the faces of cubes and other rectangular prisms and how they come together to form the whole

Vocabulary

pattern

Today's Plan		Materials
DISCUSSION ❶ **Patterns for 1-Cube Boxes** 🕐 15 MIN 👥 CLASS		• Student-made patterns for 1-cube boxes (from Session 2.1); chart paper (optional)
ACTIVITY ❷ **Patterns for 2-Cube Boxes** 🕐 45 MIN 👥 PAIRS		• M16* • Scissors; cubes; poster: "Open-Box Pattern Rules" (from Session 2.1)
SESSION FOLLOW-UP ❸ **Daily Practice and Homework**		• *Student Activity Book,* p. 19 • *Student Math Handbook,* p. 131 • M16*; cubes

*See *Materials to Prepare,* p. 49.

Ten-Minute Math

More or Less? Write the problem 1,500 − 495 on the board. Students estimate the difference and decide if it is more or less than 1,000. Select students to share their strategies. Ask:

- What did you pay attention to when you looked at these numbers? Did you use addition or subtraction to estimate this problem? What did you add/subtract first?

Then ask:

- How far from the exact answer was your estimate?

If some students mentally calculated the exact answer, ask them to share the answer and their strategy with the class. If time remains, pose additional similar problems such as: 550 − 400.

Differentiation

❶ **English Language Learners** To encourage English Language Learners to participate in this discussion, you can have them practice explaining their strategies with a partner in advance. These practice sessions will also provide useful reinforcement of key vocabulary and concepts, which will help English Language Learners better understand the whole-class discussion.

DISCUSSION

① Patterns for 1-Cube Boxes

15 MIN   CLASS

Math Focus Points for Discussion

◆ Determining the number and shapes of the faces of cubes and other rectangular prisms and how they come together to form the whole

For this discussion, students should have the patterns they made for 1-cube boxes in Session 2.1. Ask for volunteers to share their patterns.

What did you need to think about as you designed open boxes to hold one cube?

As students share their strategies, have them post their patterns on the chalkboard or on a sheet of chart paper so that everyone can see them. For each pattern posted, ask the students whether they agree that it works. When there is disagreement, students should justify their patterns.❶

Sometimes students will post duplicate patterns. In such cases, duplicates should be placed under the originals. Discuss which patterns count as duplicates. Any congruent pattern that can be turned or flipped to fit directly over the other pattern is a duplicate. However, for the purpose of this activity, allow students to decide what criteria to use.

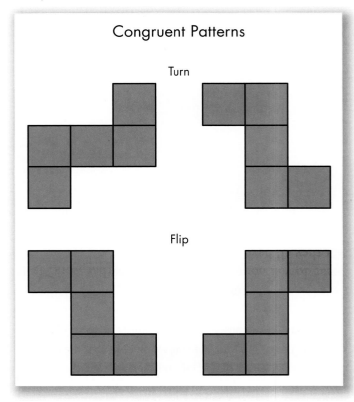

Congruent Patterns

Turn

Flip

What do you notice about the patterns that work? Is there anything that they all have in common?

Students should notice that all of the patterns contain five squares. If the reason for this has not already come up in the discussion (the cube has 6 square faces and one is uncovered in the open box), ask students why they think this is true.

Tell students that in the next activity they will be making patterns for 2-cube boxes.

Professional Development

② **Dialogue Box:** Making Patterns for the 2-Cube Solid, p. 112

Teaching Note

③ **Displaying Patterns for the 2-Cube Solid**
Because students create a variety of patterns for the 2-cube solid, many teachers find ways to display this work. After the discussion in the next session, you can set up a section of a bulletin board or chalkboard where students can attach their patterns. Students should glue or tape only the bottom squares of the patterns to the display so that the patterns can be folded into boxes.

ACTIVITY

②Patterns for 2-Cube Boxes

45 MIN   PAIRS

Distribute two 1-inch cubes and eight copies of One-Inch Grid Paper (M16), to each pair of students.

We just discussed the patterns you made to build boxes for 1 cube. Now you'll work with a partner to make open boxes for 2 cubes, following the same rules you used for the 1-cube boxes.

Direct students' attention to the "Open-Box Pattern Rules" poster and briefly review each rule.

Students still do not tape their patterns into boxes at this point because they are designing patterns, not boxes. However, they may cut out each pattern, fold it, and place the inch cubes inside to make sure that it works. Let students know that they will share and discuss their patterns at the beginning of the next session.② ③

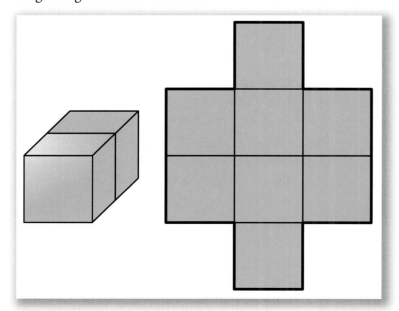

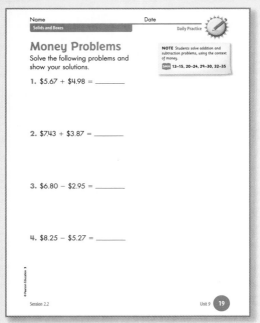

Money Problems
Solve the following problems and show your solutions.

NOTE Students solve addition and subtraction problems, using the context of money.

1. $5.67 + $4.98 = _____

2. $7.43 + $3.87 = _____

3. $6.80 − $2.95 = _____

4. $8.25 − $5.27 = _____

▲ Student Activity Book, p. 19

ONGOING ASSESSMENT: Observing Students at Work

Students use visualization and spatial reasoning skills to design open boxes for rectangular prisms made from two cubes.

- **Are the students following the rules for the patterns?**

- **Are they making several patterns for a 2-cube box?**

- **Do they use cubes or are they able to visualize the patterns without the cubes?**

- **Can they alter a pattern that does not work to make one that does?** Can they alter a pattern that does work to make another that works?

- **Do students recognize that the number of squares in their patterns depends on whether the base for the pattern is 1 or 2 cubes across?**

DIFFERENTIATION: Supporting the Range of Learners

Extension Students who have made many patterns for the 2-cube box can try patterns for 3-cube boxes.

SESSION FOLLOW-UP
3 Daily Practice and Homework

 Daily Practice: For ongoing review, have students complete *Student Activity Book* page 19.

 Homework: Challenge students to try to make more patterns that will make a 2-cube box. Some students who have already made many patterns may try 3-cube boxes instead. Students will need several sheets of One-Inch Grid Paper (M16), and, if possible, two or three cubes.

 Student Math Handbook: Students and families may use *Student Math Handbook* page 131 for reference and review. See pages 115–117 in the back of this unit.

Patterns for Triangular Pyramids

Math Focus Points

◆ Determining the number and shapes of the faces of cubes and other rectangular prisms and how they come together to form the whole

◆ Designing patterns that make nets for triangular pyramids

◆ Determining the number and shapes of the faces of a triangular pyramid and how they come together to form the whole

Vocabulary

net

Today's Plan		Materials
① DISCUSSION **What Do We Notice About Our Patterns?**	20 MIN CLASS	• Student-made patterns for 2-cube boxes (from Session 2.2); chart paper (optional)
② ACTIVITY **Patterns for Triangular Pyramids**	40 MIN PAIRS	• *Student Activity Book*, p. 20 • M17*; M13 (from Session 1.5; optional) • Scissors; geometric solids (optional)
③ SESSION FOLLOW-UP **Daily Practice and Homework**		• *Student Activity Book*, pp. 21–22 • *Student Math Handbook*, p. 131

*See *Materials to Prepare,* p. 49.

Ten-Minute Math

More or Less? Write the problem $20.00 — $6.75 on the board. Students estimate the difference and decide if it is more or less than $10.00. Select students to share their strategies. Ask:

• What did you pay attention to when you looked at these numbers? What did you do first? Did you use combinations that you know equal $1.00 or $10.00 to help you?

Then ask:

• How far from the exact answer was your estimate?

If some students mentally calculated the exact answer, ask them to share the answer and their strategy with the class. If time remains, pose additional similar problems such as: $15.00 — ($2.36 + $2.60).

DISCUSSION

What Do We Notice About Our Patterns?

20 MIN   CLASS

Math Focus Points for Discussion

◆ Determining the number and shapes of the faces of cubes and other rectangular prisms and how they come together to form the whole

Begin this session with a discussion of the patterns students found for 2-cube boxes. They will need the patterns they made in Session 2.2. Have students show their patterns and explain why they work.

Follow the procedure for the discussion in Session 2.2, asking students to share their strategies for making boxes and having them display them. Again, ask students whether they agree that each pattern works. When there is disagreement, students should justify their ideas. Allow time for students to talk through their ideas to see whether they can come to an agreement before folding the patterns to see whether they make the appropriate box.

Students should notice that all of the patterns that work contain either eight or nine squares.

Why is it possible to have eight *or* nine squares in a pattern that works?

Listen for understanding that the number of squares in the pattern depends on whether the open top is one or two squares across.❶

Students might say:

"I stacked my cubes one on top of the other. That means that the open top was only one square, so I had to cover nine squares."

"I put my cubes next to each other, so the open top was two squares. I had to cover eight squares."

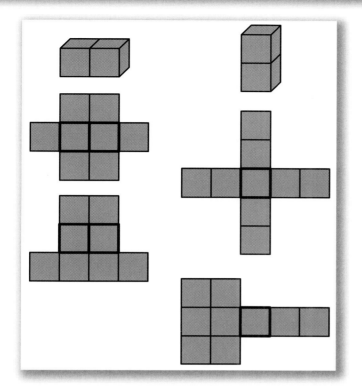

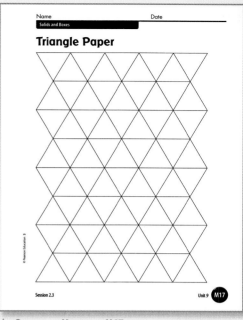

Name _____ Date _____
Solids and Boxes

Triangle Paper

Session 2.3   Unit 9 **M17**

▲ **Resource Masters, M17**

Math Note

❷ **Terminology—*Nets*** The geometric term for a closed pattern that can be folded to create the surface of the solid is *net*. Explaining and using this term with students may help them avoid confusion between this task and designing open boxes.

ACTIVITY

❷ Patterns for Triangular Pyramids

40 MIN   **PAIRS**

In this activity, students use triangular grid paper Triangle Paper (M17) to design patterns for *closed* boxes that will hold a triangular pyramid where all four of the faces are equilateral triangles.

Make sure that students understand that a closed box pattern will cover all of the faces of the pyramid, unlike the open boxes for the rectangular solids in which one face was left uncovered.❷

Because a triangular pyramid is not part of the set of geometric solids students have been using, take some time to make sure that students have a visual image of what a triangular pyramid looks like.

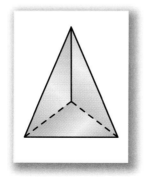

Math Note

❸ "Regular" Triangular Pyramids The triangle paper that students use for this activity is composed of equilateral triangles. Therefore, the pyramids that students construct will all be "regular" triangular pyramids, meaning triangular pyramids in which all of the faces are equal.

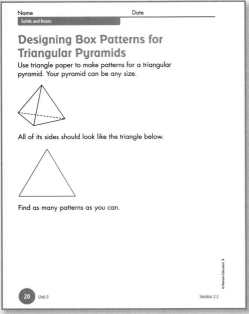

▲ **Student Activity Book, p. 20**

When we worked with the set of geometric solids, one of the solids in that set was a square pyramid. Who remembers why we call the pyramid in the set a "square" pyramid?

Make sure that students understand that a pyramid is named for the shape of the face that forms its base.

Today we are going to make nets that will hold triangular pyramids. What do you think a triangular pyramid looks like? What shape would form the base of a triangular pyramid?

To make sure that students have a visual image of a triangular pyramid, direct their attention to the picture of a triangular pyramid on *Student Activity Book* page 20.

Explain to students that they can make different-sized pyramids and that they should fold, but not tape, their nets into boxes to check their work.

Students work in pairs on this activity. When they have a variety of patterns, post different ideas on the board and discuss them, testing any patterns that are challenged and encouraging the designers to explain and defend their patterns.

Several student-designed patterns are shown below. The patterns make two different-sized pyramids but each has four faces that are equilateral triangles.❸

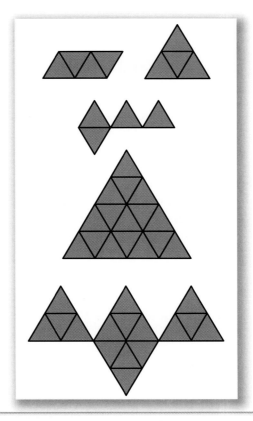

ONGOING ASSESSMENT: Observing Students at Work

Students use spatial visualization skills to create nets for triangular pyramids in which all four faces are equilateral triangles.

- **Do students understand the task of creating a net for a triangular pyramid?** Do they consider the structure of the pyramid (4 triangular faces) to construct a net that will fold to cover all four faces?

- **Are they able to create nets for pyramids of varying sizes?**

DIFFERENTIATION: Supporting the Range of Learners

Extension For most students, creating nets for triangular pyramids will be a sufficient challenge for this session. Some students, however, may want to try making nets for other geometric solids. These students can use Geometric Solids (M13) for reference and might need to use wooden solids to trace the faces.

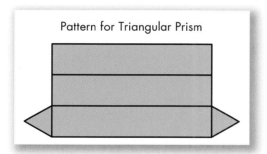

Pattern for Triangular Prism

SESSION FOLLOW-UP
③ Daily Practice and Homework

 Daily Practice: For ongoing review, have students complete *Student Activity Book* page 21.

 Homework: Students solve subtraction problems with 3-digit numbers on *Student Activity Book* page 22.

 Student Math Handbook: Students and families may use *Student Math Handbook* page 131 for reference and review. See pages 115–117 in the back of this unit.

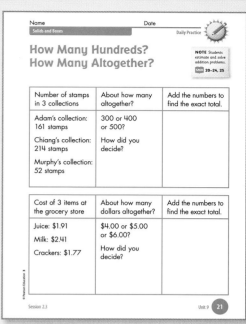
▲ Student Activity Book, p. 21

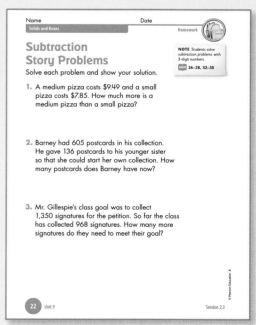
▲ Student Activity Book, p. 22

Mathematical Emphases

Features of Shape Translating between 2-dimensional and 3-dimensional shapes

Math Focus Points

◆ Communicating about the spatial relationships in 3-D shapes

◆ Decomposing images of 3-D shapes and then recombining them to make a given structure

Volume Structuring rectangular prisms and determining their volume

Math Focus Points

◆ Determining the number of cubes that will fit in the box made by a given pattern

◆ Designing patterns for boxes that will hold a given number of cubes

◆ Seeing that the cubes filling a rectangular prism can be decomposed into congruent layers

How Many Cubes in a Box?

	Student Activity Book	Student Math Handbook	Professional Development: Read Ahead of Time	
SESSION 3.1 p. 68				
Finding the Number of Cubes in a Box Students organize visual images to build cube structures that are briefly shown on the overhead. They examine the structure and volume of rectangular prisms by working with patterns for open boxes.	23–24	132–133	• **Dialogue Box:** Seeing Cube Buildings in Our Minds, p. 113 • **Teacher Note:** Strategies for Finding the Number of Cubes in a Box, p. 96	
SESSION 3.2 p. 74				
12-Cube Boxes Students reflect on the structure of box patterns through designing rectangular boxes to hold exactly 12 cubes.	25–26	132–133	• **Teacher Note:** Strategies for Boxes That Hold 12 Cubes, p. 100	
SESSION 3.3 p. 80				
Assessment: Patterns from the Bottom Up Students complete designs for box patterns, given the shape of the bottoms of the boxes. They are assessed on their ability to determine the number of cubes that will fit in a given box pattern.	27–28	132–133	• **Teacher Note:** Assessment: Writing About How Many Cubes, p. 97	
SESSION 3.4 p. 85				
Riddles About Boxes Students discuss strategies for completing box patterns when given the pattern for the bottom of the box. They continue to develop understanding of the structure of rectangular prisms through Math Workshop activities.	29–31	132–133		
SESSION 3.5 p. 91				
End-of-Unit Assessment Students are assessed on their knowledge and understanding of the 3-D geometry unit.	33–34	129–130, 132–133	• **Teacher Note:** End-of-Unit Assessment, p. 101	

Ten-Minute Math See page 14 for an overview.

Quick Images: 3-D
- T104–T106, *Quick Images* Cut apart each image.
- Connecting cubes (20 per student)

Materials to Gather	Materials to Prepare
• **T107, Pattern A** • **Connecting cubes** (20 per student) • **Scissors** (1 per student or pair)	• **T104–T106, *Quick Images*** Cut apart each image. • **M21–M25, How Many Cubes?** Make copies. (1 per student)
• **Poster: "Open-Box Pattern Rules"** (from Session 2.1) • **Connecting cubes** (60 per pair) • **Scissors** (1 per student or pair) • **Tape** (1 roll per student or pair) • **Student-made boxes for 12 cubes**	• **M27, Three-Quarter-Inch Grid Paper** Make copies. (5 per student, plus extras)
• **T108, Making Boxes from the Bottom Up** • **Connecting cubes** (as needed) • **Scissors** (1 per student or pair) • **Tape** (1 roll per student or pair)	• **M27, Three-Quarter-Inch Grid Paper** Make copies. (as needed; optional) • **M28–M31, Making Boxes from the Bottom Up** Make copies. (1 per student) • **M32, Assessment: Writing About How Many Cubes** Make copies. (1 per student)
• **T108, Making Boxes from the Bottom Up** • **Connecting cubes** (as needed) • **Scissors** (1 per student or pair) • **Tape** (1 roll per pair) • **Chart: "Multiplication and Division"** (from *Equal Groups*, Unit 5) Display the chart you made during your study of multiplication and division in Unit 5.	• **M27, Three-Quarter-Inch Grid Paper** Make copies. (2 per student for homework; additional copies as needed during session) • **M33–M35, More Boxes from the Bottom Up** Make copies. (1 per student)
• **Connecting cubes** (as needed) • **Geometric solids** (from Session 1.1; as needed)	• **M36–M40, End-of-Unit Assessment** Make copies. (1 per student)

 Overhead Transparency

Finding the Number of Cubes in a Box

Math Focus Points

◆ Communicating about spatial relationships

◆ Decomposing images of 3-D shapes and then recombining them to make a given structure

◆ Determining the number of cubes that will fit in the box made by a given pattern

Today's Plan		Materials
ACTIVITY ❶ *Quick Images: Cube Buildings*	20 MIN INDIVIDUALS CLASS	• T104–T106* • Connecting cubes
ACTIVITY ❷ Determining the Number of Cubes in a Box	25 MIN PAIRS	• M21–M25* • Connecting cubes; scissors
DISCUSSION ❸ Strategies for Determining the Number of Cubes	15 MIN CLASS	• T107
SESSION FOLLOW-UP ❹ Daily Practice and Homework		• *Student Activity Book,* pp. 23–24 • *Student Math Handbook,* pp. 132–133

*See *Materials to Prepare,* p. 67.

Ten-Minute Math

NOTE: The Ten-Minute Math activity for this unit, *Quick Images: 3-D,* is introduced in this session. Plan to do today's Ten-Minute Math sometime after math class, or if it is not possible, do the other Ten-Minute Math activity in this unit, *Practicing Place Value,* with which your students are familiar.

Quick Images: 3-D Show Images 4 and 5 (one at a time) from *Quick Images* (T104), and follow the procedure for the basic routine. For each image, students discuss how they built their structures, including any revisions they made after each viewing. Ask questions such as:

• How did you remember the parts of the image? What did you notice about the relationship of the parts of the image? What helped you remember the whole image, so you could build your structure?

ACTIVITY

Quick Images: Cube Buildings

20 MIN INDIVIDUALS CLASS

Place Image 1 from *Quick Images* (T104) on the overhead projector with the projector turned off.

Give each student 20 connecting cubes. All students should be seated facing the overhead screen.

Today we're going to try picturing cube buildings in our heads. I will flash a picture of a cube building on the overhead for 3 seconds. Look at it carefully. When I turn off the overhead, try to see the picture in your mind. Then use your cubes to make the building that you saw. Don't start building until I turn the overhead off. I will flash the picture again after everyone has had time to try building it. ❶

Turn the projector on and show Image 1 for 3 seconds. Turn the projector off [or cover the image] and give students time to work with their cubes. After you see that most of the building activity has stopped, call students' attention to the overhead and flash the picture again for another 3 seconds. They should have built as much as they can until they see the picture on the screen again.

After the second flash of a Quick Image, *most students can finish their cube buildings.*

When the building activity subsides again, show the picture a third time. This time, leave it visible so that all students can complete or revise their solutions.

After students are satisfied that their buildings are complete, ask them to describe how they saw the picture as they looked at it on successive flashes. ❷

Teaching Note

❶ **Why *Quick Images*?** It is important to keep the picture up for as close to 3 seconds as possible. If you show the picture too long, students will build from the picture rather than their image of it. If you show it too briefly, they will not have time to form a mental image. Stress the importance of studying the figure carefully while it is visible so that students can then build it from their mental image.

Professional Development

❷ **Dialogue Box:** Seeing Cube Buildings in Our Minds, p. 113

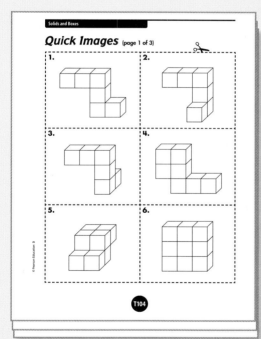

▲ Transparencies, T104–T106

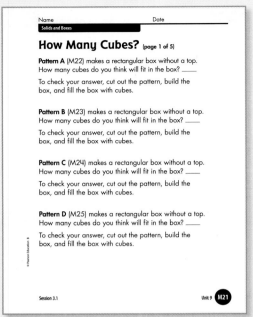

▲ Resource Masters, M21

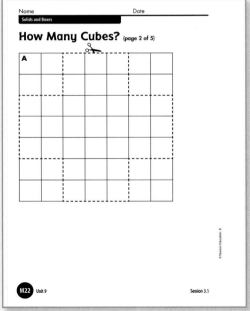

▲ Resource Masters, M22

What picture did you have in your mind when you saw the image the first time?

What did you pay attention to that helped you form that picture?

How did you know how many cubes to use to make your building?

What did you notice when you saw the image the second time? The third time?

Did you need to make any changes?

Continue the same activity with Images 2 and 3. The transparency provides more images than you will need in this session. Use these additional images as Ten-Minute Math activities during the remainder of this unit.

After students have had time to construct the cube building in Image 3, ask them to save the building and to write a description of how they saw it in their mind. This will give you a quick informal assessment of all students' thinking. Check that students' buildings are correctly configured and examine their descriptions to see how they are organizing their images. Are they seeing the images as wholes or as parts, or are they counting parts?

Most students should be able to make a *Quick Images* cube building after two flashes of the picture. All students should be able to build them after the picture is left visible.

ONGOING ASSESSMENT: Observing Students at Work

Students make a cube building from images projected on the overhead.

- **How are students seeing the images?** Are they decomposing the shape by parts? By simpler geometric shapes? Do they see the image as a whole?

- **Do the students recognize that Images 1, 2, and 3 are the same with the exception of the bottom right cube, which moves from the right in Image 1 to the front in Image 2 and to the back in Image 3?**

DIFFERENTIATION: Supporting the Range of Learners

(Intervention) Some students will only be able to make the building the third time (when the image is left up on the screen). Encourage these students to listen to other students' strategies and to find an organization strategy for the next picture.

ACTIVITY

② Determining the Number of Cubes in a Box

25 MIN   PAIRS

Direct students' attention to the five pages How Many Cubes? (M21–M25). Each page contains a pattern for a different rectangular box, open at the top.

These pages show patterns for open boxes, boxes without tops, like the ones you made to hold one or two cubes, except that these patterns make boxes to hold many cubes. Work with a partner and think about how many of these cubes [show a connecting cube] each box will hold without actually placing the cubes inside it. Start with Pattern A. Look carefully at the bottom and sides of the pattern. Write your idea on the line.

Make sure that students understand that their ideas should not be mere guesses but should be based on their analysis of how the cubes will fit into the folded box.

To check whether your idea is correct, cut out the pattern and fold it to make the box. Then fill it with cubes. Make sure that you connect the cubes so they will fit in the box.❸

Students then go on to the next pattern. They consider how many cubes will fit before building the box, and then build it to check their initial answers. They do the same for the third box and finally the fourth. This procedure encourages students to keep refining their strategies.❹

ONGOING ASSESSMENT: Observing Students at Work

Students develop and use visualization skills by first estimating how many cubes will fit into given box patterns and then making the boxes and filling them with cubes.

- **What strategies are students using to determine how many cubes will fit in the box?**

- **Are some students confusing the number of squares in the box pattern with the number of cubes that will fill the box?**

- **Are they considering the number of cubes that make up the bottom layer and then looking at the sides to determine the number of layers?**

❸ **Connecting the Cubes** The faces of the $\frac{3}{4}$-inch connecting cubes match the size of the squares in the box patterns on the pages. If the cubes are connected, they should fit into the boxes perfectly. Take a moment to demonstrate the proper way to connect the cubes. Build a $2 \times 3 \times 2$ cube configuration and ask students to do the same. Help any students who are having difficulty with this task.

Professional Development

❹ **Teacher Note:** Strategies for Finding the Number of Cubes in a Box, p. 96

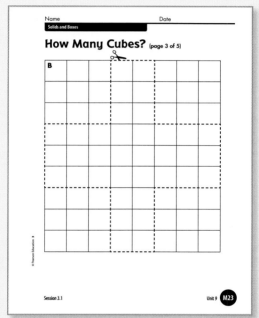

▲ Resource Masters, M23

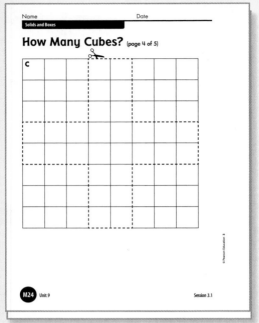

Name _____ Date _____

Solids and Boxes

How Many Cubes? (page 4 of 5)

c

M24 Unit 9   Session 3.1

▲ **Resource Masters, M24–M25**

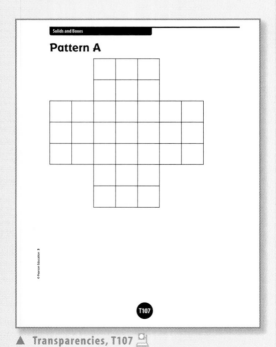

Solids and Boxes

Pattern A

T107

▲ **Transparencies, T107**

DIFFERENTIATION: Supporting the Range of Learners

Intervention Some students will count each square on a pattern and guess that the box will hold that number of cubes. For example, Pattern A consists of 33 squares, but when folded makes a box that will hold 18 cubes. Help these students think about what the squares on the pattern represent and what the space inside the box is like when it is folded.

I see that you think that Pattern A would make a box for 33 cubes. If you put 33 cubes on Pattern A, what will happen when you try to fold the box? Will all the cubes fit inside?

Have the students cut out and fold the pattern.

How many cubes fit in the bottom of the box? How many more cubes do you need to fill the box? What do you think the squares on the side of the pattern can tell you?

DISCUSSION

3 **Strategies for Determining the Number of Cubes**

15 MIN   CLASS

Math Focus Points for Discussion

◆ Determining the number of cubes that will fit in a box made by a given pattern

Show the transparency of Pattern A (T107).

How many cubes did you think would fit into the box made from Pattern A before you actually cut it out? How did you decide on that number?

Students' strategies will vary. Some students will have correctly said 18 cubes, having examined the box pattern to determine that there are 9 cubes in the bottom layer and 9 more cubes in the top layer. Others may have counted the squares in the pattern, getting 33. It may seem that they have misconstrued the problem, thinking about squares rather than cubes. However, they may have been thinking that a cube fits on each square and that when the pattern is folded, these cubes will fit the box exactly.

What happened when you cut out and folded the box? Did you have to change your thinking? Why were some of your ideas different from the number of cubes that actually fit into the box?

Students might say:

"We thought the box would hold 9 cubes because we just counted the squares on the bottom. Then when the box was folded, we saw that there was room for another layer of 9 cubes. That's 18 cubes in all."

"We counted all the squares and got 33, but that many cubes didn't fit when the box was folded."

Students will develop their understanding of the relationship between the squares in box patterns and the volume of the resulting boxes as they continue the work of this investigation.

4 SESSION FOLLOW-UP
Daily Practice and Homework

 Daily Practice: For reinforcement of this unit's content, have students complete *Student Activity Book* page 23.

 Homework: Students solve subtraction problems with 3-digit numbers on *Student Activity Book* page 24.

 Student Math Handbook: Students and families may use *Student Math Handbook* pages 132–133 for reference and review. See pages 115–117 in the back of this unit.

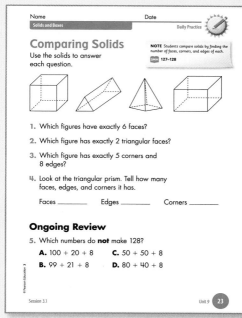

Name _____ Date _____
Solids and Boxes — Daily Practice

Comparing Solids
Use the solids to answer each question.

NOTE Students compare solids by finding the number of faces, corners, and edges of each.
SMH 127–128

1. Which figures have exactly 6 faces?

2. Which figure has exactly 2 triangular faces?

3. Which figure has exactly 5 corners and 8 edges?

4. Look at the triangular prism. Tell how many faces, edges, and corners it has.

Faces _____ Edges _____ Corners _____

Ongoing Review

5. Which numbers do **not** make 128?

   A. 100 + 20 + 8   **C.** 50 + 50 + 8
   B. 99 + 21 + 8   **D.** 80 + 40 + 8

Session 3.1   Unit 9 23

▲ **Student Activity Book, p. 23**

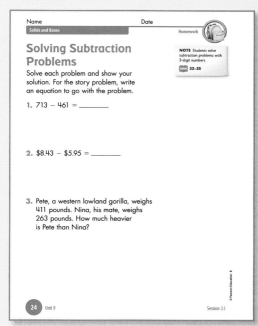

Name _____ Date _____
Solids and Boxes — Homework

Solving Subtraction Problems
Solve each problem and show your solution. For the story problem, write an equation to go with the problem.

NOTE Students solve subtraction problems with 3-digit numbers.
SMH 32–35

1. 713 − 461 = _____

2. $8.43 − $5.95 = _____

3. Pete, a western lowland gorilla, weighs 411 pounds. Nina, his mate, weighs 263 pounds. How much heavier is Pete than Nina?

24 Unit 9   Session 3.1

▲ **Student Activity Book, p. 24**

12-Cube Boxes

Math Focus Points

◆ Designing patterns for boxes that will hold a given number of cubes

◆ Seeing that the cubes filling a rectangular prism can be decomposed into congruent layers

Today's Plan			Materials
ACTIVITY **①** **Designing Boxes to Hold 12 Cubes**	45 MIN	PAIRS	• M27* • Connecting cubes; scissors; tape; poster: "Open-Box Pattern Rules" (from Session 2.1)
DISCUSSION **②** **Strategies for Our Boxes**	15 MIN	CLASS	• Student-made boxes for 12 cubes
SESSION FOLLOW-UP **③** **Daily Practice and Homework**			• *Student Activity Book,* pp. 25–26 • M27* • *Student Math Handbook,* pp. 132–133

*See *Materials to Prepare,* p. 67.

Ten-Minute Math

Quick Images: 3-D Show Images 6 and 7 (one at a time) from *Quick Images* (T104–T105), and follow the procedure for the basic routine. After students have seen both images and discussed how they built their structures, ask questions to focus on the relationships between the two figures. For example:

• Are there any parts of these two images that are the same? What's different about them? What did you notice about the relationship of the parts of the image?

ACTIVITY

Designing Boxes to Hold 12 Cubes

45 MIN   PAIRS

Yesterday, you had four box patterns and you figured out how many cubes would fit into those boxes. Today you're going to design your own patterns for boxes. The task is to design open rectangular boxes that will hold exactly 12 cubes. The goal is to make as many different boxes as possible. You can use cubes to help you make your designs.

There are many different boxes that students can make to solve this problem. Two boxes that hold the same cube configuration are considered different when their open tops are different. For instance, there are two different boxes that will contain the $1 \times 1 \times 12$ cube configuration. One has a 1×1 open top; the other has a 1×12 open top.

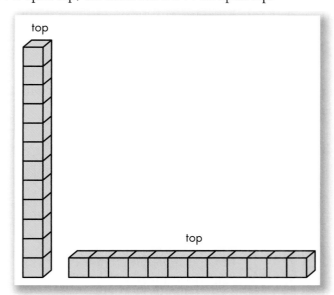

Similarly, there are three boxes that contain a $1 \times 2 \times 6$ cube configuration: one with a 1×2 open top; one with a 1×6 open top; and one with a 2×6 open top.

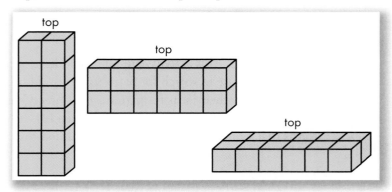

Professional Development

❶ **Teacher Note:** Strategies for Boxes That Hold 12 Cubes, p. 100

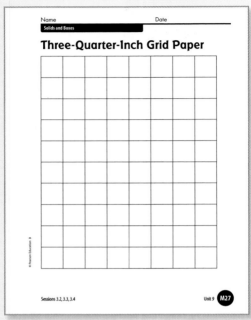

▲ Resource Masters, M27

Students might also make boxes for a $1 \times 3 \times 4$ cube configuration. There are three different boxes that will hold this configuration: one with a 3×4 open top, one with a 1×4 open top, and one with a 1×3 open top.

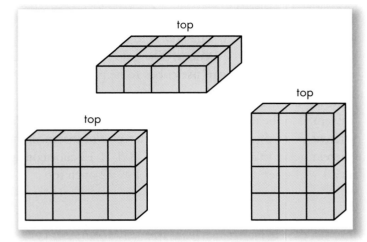

Lastly, students might make two different boxes for a $2 \times 2 \times 3$ cube configuration: one with a 2×3 open top and one with a 2×2 open top.

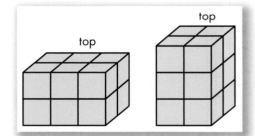

Some students may interpret this activity as finding many different patterns for the same configuration and positioning of cubes (e.g., a $1 \times 2 \times 6$ with a 2×6 open top). Encourage these students to also make box patterns for the cube configuration positioned with different open tops (e.g., 1×6 and 1×2 open tops). These students can also be encouraged to find and make boxes for different configurations of the 12 cubes (e.g., $1 \times 1 \times 12$ and $1 \times 3 \times 4$ configurations).❶

Students work in pairs on this activity, but all should have their own supply of grid paper to use to search for patterns. To find boxes that hold 12 cubes, students draw their ideas for patterns on Three-Quarter-Inch Grid Paper (M27), cut them out, fold them, and then fill them with cubes. Patterns that work should be taped together into boxes and saved.

Encourage students to use cubes whenever they need them, from the early design stages to the checking of final patterns. Some students will benefit by building a rectangular structure from 12 cubes first, placing it on the grid, and trying to draw the pattern for the box. As students are taping their boxes, suggest that they leave one face untaped, making it easier to put in and take out cubes.

Encourage students, when they can, to make their boxes out of whole sheets of paper rather than separate pieces. Explain that some boxes for 12 cubes will require that they tape several sheets of paper together. For example, neither of the boxes for a $1 \times 12 \times 1$ cube configuration can be made from an 8×10 grid without cutting and taping.

Occasionally, students will design nonrectangular boxes. Acknowledge such creative solutions, but remind students that rectangular boxes are needed for shipping and stacking.

It is not necessary that students discover all possible boxes. What is important is that they remain productively engaged in generating and evaluating new ideas for boxes and deciding when two boxes are the same or different.

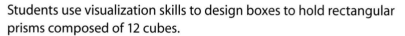

ONGOING ASSESSMENT: Observing Students at Work

Students use visualization skills to design boxes to hold rectangular prisms composed of 12 cubes.

- **What strategies are students using to design a box to hold 12 cubes?** Do they think about layers? Do they use knowledge of factors of 12 to help them conceptualize their boxes?

- **Do they work with different configurations of 12 cubes, or are they making multiple patterns for the same configuration?** Are they designing boxes with different open faces for the same configuration?

- **If students design patterns that do not work, do they consider how to change the patterns or simply discard them and start again?**

Circulate as students are working to observe their strategies and help them with any difficulties they might be having. Sometimes, mentioning layers will help students design the box patterns.

- **How many cubes are in the bottom layer?**

- **How many layers are there?**

- **How can you show the number of layers with the sides of your pattern?**

DIFFERENTIATION: Supporting the Range of Learners

Extension Students who quickly find patterns for a given configuration of 12 cubes positioned with different open tops should be encouraged to try a different configuration. If a student has successfully made boxes with different open faces for a 1 × 3 × 4 arrangement, ask these questions:

Is there a different rectangular prism that you can make with 12 cubes? What boxes can you make for that prism?

DISCUSSION
Strategies for Our Boxes

15 MIN   CLASS

Math Focus Points for Discussion

◆ Designing patterns for boxes that will hold a given number of cubes

Call students back together to share their strategies. Begin by holding up a 1 × 3 × 4 rectangular prism and asking whether any students made boxes for that configuration of 12 cubes. As students share their boxes, ask questions such as the following:

What did you have to pay attention to when you made your boxes?

How did you decide what the bottom of your box would look like?

Did the bottom help you figure out the sides? How?

As students respond, listen for understanding of how the base of the box pattern determines the number of layers the box will contain. For example, students who chose to make a box with a 3 × 4 base should recognize that the box will be only one layer high. Other students might make a box with a 1 × 4 base.

Students might say:

"I know that there are 4 cubes on the bottom. Two layers make 8 cubes and one more layer makes 12. So my box needed to be 3 layers high. 3 × 4 = 12."

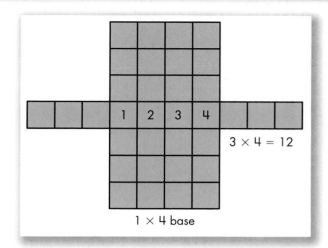

$3 \times 4 = 12$

1×4 base

When a strategy like the last one has been shared, ask a follow-up question.

What if you made the bottom with three cubes? How many layers would your box need to have?

Be aware that some students may still be positioning the cubes on the grid paper and counting the cubes on the sides to figure out the number of layers. As they listen to their classmates' strategies, these students may begin to recognize that they can use their knowledge of factors and multiples of 12 to determine the number of layers each box must have.

SESSION FOLLOW-UP

③ Daily Practice and Homework

 Daily Practice: For reinforcement of this unit's content, have students complete *Student Activity Book* page 25.

 Homework: Each student needs *Student Activity Book* page 26 and three copies of Three-Quarter-Inch Grid Paper (M27) to fold into boxes to hold a $2 \times 6 \times 1$ solid.

 Student Math Handbook: Students and families may use *Student Math Handbook* pages 132–133 for reference and review. See pages 115–117 in the back of this unit.

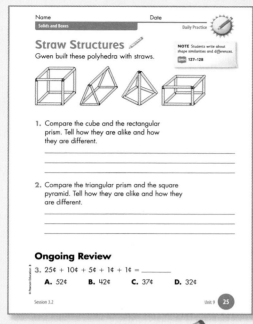

▲ **Student Activity Book, p. 25**

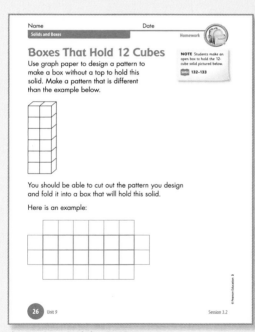

▲ **Student Activity Book, p. 26**

Assessment: Patterns from the Bottom Up

Math Focus Points

◆ Designing patterns for boxes that will hold a given number of cubes

◆ Seeing that the cubes filling a rectangular prism can be decomposed into congruent layers

◆ Determining the number of cubes that will fit in the box made by a given pattern

Vocabulary
volume

Today's Plan		Materials
ACTIVITY **❶ Introducing Patterns from the Bottom Up**	15 MIN INDIVIDUALS CLASS	• M28*; T108 • Connecting cubes; scissors; tape
ACTIVITY **❷ Patterns from the Bottom Up**	30 MIN PAIRS CLASS	• M27 (optional)*; M28–M31* • Connecting cubes; scissors; tape
ASSESSMENT ACTIVITY **❸ Writing About How Many Cubes**	✓ 15 MIN INDIVIDUALS	• M32*
SESSION FOLLOW-UP **❹ Daily Practice and Homework**		• *Student Activity Book*, pp. 27–28 • *Student Math Handbook*, pp. 132–133

*See *Materials to Prepare*, p. 67.

Ten-Minute Math

Quick Images: 3-D Show Images 8 and 9 (one at a time) from *Quick Images* (T105), and follow the procedure for the basic routine. After students have seen both images and discussed how they built their structures, ask questions to focus on the relationships between the two figures. For example:

• Are there any parts of these two images that are the same? What's different about them? What did you notice about the relationship of the parts of the image?

ACTIVITY

1 Introducing Patterns from the Bottom Up

15 MIN INDIVIDUALS CLASS

Designing box patterns is a challenging task. Students will develop strategies for designing patterns through repeated experiences, discussion with others, and teacher guidance. Students need copies of Making Boxes from the Bottom Up (M28).

Display the transparency of Making Boxes from the Bottom Up (T108).

This is the bottom of a rectangular box that contains exactly 6 cubes. The box has no top. Draw the sides to complete the pattern for the box. You can use cubes to help you if you like.

After students have spent some time working, ask them to share their strategies.

Somebody show us on the overhead how you completed the pattern.

- *How did you decide what the sides would look like?*

- *How many layers does the pattern have?*

- *How did you know how many layers there would be?*

- *Did anyone come up with a different pattern?*

Let students show and discuss whatever patterns they have designed.

Make a box from your pattern and test it by filling it with cubes. Did the cubes fit in the box made from your pattern?

Because students have already drawn their patterns, this should take no longer than 5 minutes.

If the pattern drawn on the overhead was not correct, ask a student to draw the correct pattern.

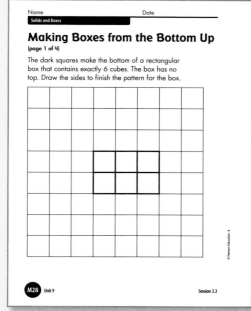

▲ Resource Masters, M28; T108

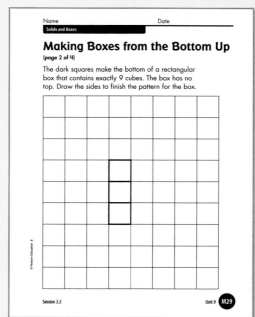

▲ Resource Masters, M29

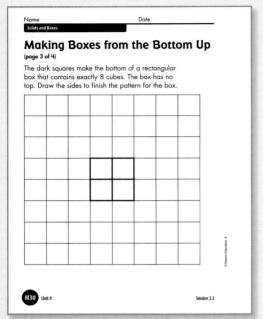

▲ Resource Masters, M30 [PORTFOLIO]

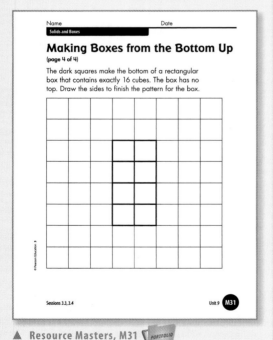

▲ Resource Masters, M31 [PORTFOLIO]

30 MIN   PAIRS   CLASS

ACTIVITY

2 Patterns from the Bottom Up

Students work on the remaining three problems on Making Boxes from the Bottom Up (M29–M31). Remind students to cut out each pattern they make and test it by filling it with cubes.

ONGOING ASSESSMENT: Observing Students at Work

Students use visualization skills and knowledge of the structure of rectangular prisms to complete box patterns when given the dimensions of the bottom of each box.

- **Are students able to accurately draw the sides of each box without using cubes?** If so, are they using knowledge of factors and multiples to determine how many layers the box must have?

- **Do they use cubes to form the bottom layer and then determine how many layers they need?** If so, do they complete the building of the cube configuration and then count the number of layers or do they use knowledge of factors and multiples to determine how many layers the box must have? For example, in the fourth problem, do they reason that, because there are eight cubes in the bottom layer, the pattern must be two layers high to hold a rectangular prism composed of 16 cubes?

As students work, continue to ask questions to encourage them to consider the relationship between the number of cubes in the bottom layer and the number of layers needed to make a box for the given number of cubes.

How did you decide what the sides would look like? How many layers does the pattern have? How did you know how many layers there would be?

DIFFERENTIATION: Supporting the Range of Learners

Intervention To make or even to understand the patterns, some students will need to make the cube configurations that fit in the boxes first. For the first problem, they would make a 2 × 3 rectangle of 6 cubes, place it on the 2 × 3 pattern for the bottom of the box, and figure out what the sides would look like. If they do not see how to proceed, point to one of the lateral sides of the structure and ask these questions:

- How tall is the building?

- How many layers does it have?

- How many cubes do you see on this side?

- Can you draw this side on the paper?

Repeat these questions for the other sides as necessary.

Some students may still be unable to make the correct patterns and will need additional practice. Make new problems on the Three-Quarter-Inch Grid Paper (M27), beginning with problems involving only one layer. For example, you can draw a 4 × 5 array and ask students to complete the pattern so that the resulting box will hold 20 cubes. You can also draw a 5 × 1 array and ask students to complete the pattern to make a 10-cube box. Then ask this question:

- What would you need to add to this pattern to make a box that holds 15 cubes?

ASSESSMENT ACTIVITY

3 Writing About How Many Cubes

15 MIN **INDIVIDUALS**

This activity enables you to assess Benchmark 2: Determine the number of cubes (volume) that will fit in the box made by a given pattern.

Distribute one copy of Assessment: Writing About How Many Cubes (M32) and a blank sheet of paper to each student.

I'm interested in finding out what strategies you use to decide on the number of cubes that will fill the box made from this box pattern without actually filling it in with the cubes. Figure out how many cubes will fit in the box without actually cutting out the box and filling it with cubes. You can write about how you determined how many cubes would fill the box directly on the box pattern if you like, or on the blank sheet of paper.❶

Professional Development

❶ **Teacher Note:** Assessment: Writing About How Many Cubes, p. 97

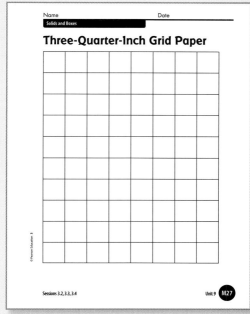

▲ Resource Masters, M27

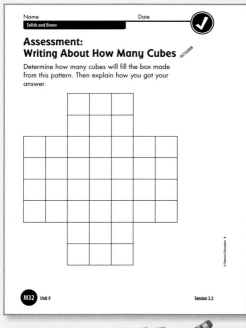

▲ Resource Masters, M32

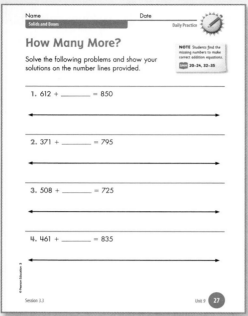

▲ **Student Activity Book, p. 27**

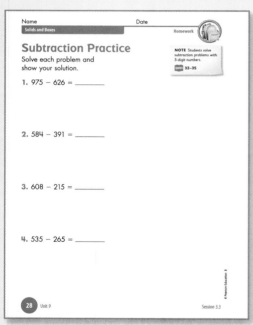

▲ **Student Activity Book, p. 28**

ONGOING ASSESSMENT: Observing Students at Work

Students use the dimensions of an open box pattern to determine the number of cubes that will fill the box.

- **Are students able to determine the number of cubes that will fill the box without actually placing cubes on the pattern, or do they build the bottom layer with cubes to help them determine the volume?**

- **Are students considering the number of cubes that make up the bottom layer and then looking at the sides to determine the number of layers?** Do some students then use addition (12 + 12 = 24) to determine the volume of the box? Do some students multiply the number of cubes in the bottom layer by the number of layers (2 × 12 = 24)?

- **Are some students still confusing the number of squares in the box pattern with the number of cubes that will fill the box?**

SESSION FOLLOW-UP
Daily Practice and Homework

 Daily Practice: For ongoing review, have students complete *Student Activity Book* page 27.

 Homework: Students solve subtraction problems with 3-digit numbers on *Student Activity Book* page 28.

 Student Math Handbook: Students and families may use *Student Math Handbook* pages 132–133 for reference and review. See pages 115–117 in the back of this unit.

Riddles About Boxes

Math Focus Points

◆ Designing patterns for boxes that will hold a given number of cubes

◆ Seeing that the cubes filling a rectangular prism can be decomposed into congruent layers

Today's Plan		Materials
DISCUSSION **① 16-Cube Box Pattern**	15 MIN CLASS	• T108
MATH WORKSHOP **② Boxes** ㉓ Riddles About Boxes ㉔ Patterns from the Bottom Up ㉕ Boxes to Hold 16 Cubes	45 MIN	㉓ • *Student Activity Book,* p.29 • M27* • Connecting cubes; chart: "Multiplication and Division" (from Unit 5, *Equal Groups*) ㉔ • M33–M35* ㉕ • M27* • Connecting cubes; scissors; tape
SESSION FOLLOW-UP **③ Daily Practice and Homework**		• *Student Activity Book,* pp. 30–31 • M27* • *Student Math Handbook,* pp. 132–133

*See *Materials to Prepare,* p. 67.

Ten-Minute Math

Quick Images: 3-D Show Images 10 and 11 (one at a time) from *Quick Images* (T105), and follow the procedure for the basic routine. For each image, students discuss how they built their structures, including any revisions they made after each viewing. Ask questions such as:

- How did you remember the parts of the image? What did you notice about the relationship of the parts of the image? What helped you remember the whole image, so you could build your structure?

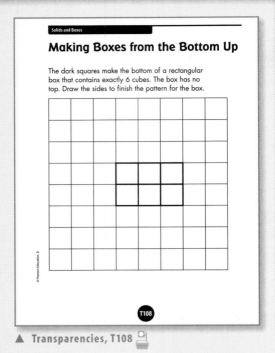

Making Boxes from the Bottom Up

The dark squares make the bottom of a rectangular box that contains exactly 6 cubes. The box has no top. Draw the sides to finish the pattern for the box.

T108

▲ Transparencies, T108

15 MIN CLASS

DISCUSSION
16-Cube Box Pattern

Math Focus Points for Discussion

◆ Designing patterns for boxes that will hold a given number of cubes
◆ Seeing that the cubes filling a rectangular prism can be decomposed into congruent layers

Display Making Boxes from the Bottom Up (T108). Ask a few students to show their patterns for the 16-cube box and to share their strategies for creating them.

Did anyone draw the sides of the 16-cube box without using cubes?

Can you explain how you knew what the sides should look like?

Who used cubes to help them finish the pattern?

Can you explain what you did?

How did building the bottom of the box help you figure out how to draw the sides?

Students might say:

 "I counted the squares and saw that the bottom of the box would hold 8 cubes. I knew that 2 layers would be 16 cubes, so that showed me that I needed to make the box 2 layers high since 8 plus 8 is 16."

 "I looked at the bottom and saw that it has 8 cubes. I know that 2 times 8 is 16, so the box had to have 2 layers."

 "I used 8 cubes to make the bottom layer and then added more cubes until I used up 16. When I finished, there were 2 layers. Then I drew the sides to show the 2 layers."

What if you wanted this box to hold 32 cubes? How many layers would you have to add to your pattern? Explain how you know.

As students respond, listen for understanding that, because each layer is composed of eight cubes, the pattern for a 32-cube box would need to have two additional layers, for a total of four layers.

MATH WORKSHOP

45 MIN

②Boxes

The Math Workshop activities in this session give students more time to work on understanding the structure of rectangular prisms. One new activity, Riddles About Boxes, is included in the Math Workshop.

Students are not expected to complete all three activities, although some may do so. Use your observations of students' work during previous sessions to assign activities on the basis of students' needs. Students who have demonstrated a good understanding of the structure of box patterns and the rectangular prisms they hold will enjoy the challenge of designing boxes for 16 cubes and may not need to complete More Boxes from the Bottom Up. Other students will benefit from more time designing patterns to hold a given number of cubes when given the bottom of the box. They should do this activity before moving on to another.

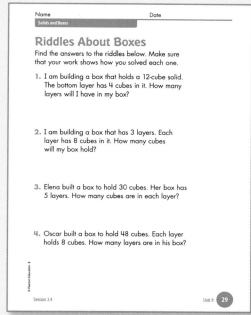

▲ **Student Activity Book, p. 29**

Riddles About Boxes

Find the answers to the riddles below. Make sure that your work shows how you solved each one.

1. I am building a box that holds a 12-cube solid. The bottom layer has 4 cubes in it. How many layers will I have in my box?

2. I am building a box that has 3 layers. Each layer has 8 cubes in it. How many cubes will my box hold?

3. Elena built a box to hold 30 cubes. Her box has 5 layers. How many cubes are in each layer?

4. Oscar built a box to hold 48 cubes. Each layer holds 8 cubes. How many layers are in his box?

②A Riddles About Boxes

INDIVIDUALS **PAIRS**

Students solve problems on *Student Activity Book* page 29. In this activity, they integrate the riddle work they did in *Equal Groups,* Unit 5, with the context of boxes to hold 3-D arrays of cubes.

ONGOING ASSESSMENT: Observing Students at Work

Students solve riddles by using their knowledge of the structure of 3-D arrays of cubes and multiplication and division.

- **Are students able to visualize these problems without using cubes and grid paper, or do they need to actually build the rectangular prisms and/or the box patterns?**

- **Do students' explanations demonstrate an understanding of the structure of box patterns designed to hold rectangular prisms made from cubes?**

- **Do students use knowledge of multiplication and division to solve these problems?**

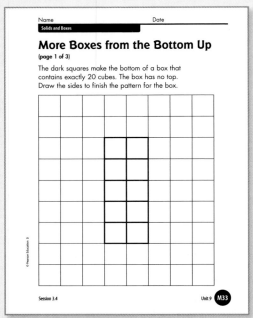

More Boxes from the Bottom Up
(page 1 of 3)

The dark squares make the bottom of a box that contains exactly 20 cubes. The box has no top. Draw the sides to finish the pattern for the box.

Session 3.4 · Unit 9 **M33**

▲ Resource Masters, M33

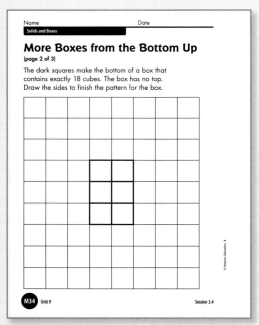

More Boxes from the Bottom Up
(page 2 of 3)

The dark squares make the bottom of a box that contains exactly 18 cubes. The box has no top. Draw the sides to finish the pattern for the box.

M34 Unit 9 · Session 3.4

▲ Resource Masters, M34

DIFFERENTIATION: Supporting the Range of Learners

Intervention Although some students will solve these problems without the use of math tools, others may benefit by using cubes and grid paper to model the action of each problem. Have these tools available for student use.

If possible, display the Multiplication and Division Chart from earlier in the year to help students think about which piece of information is missing from each riddle. It may be helpful to talk to students about the three pieces of mathematical information in a multiplication situation: the number of groups, the number in each group, and the total (product). Ask them to apply this to a box designed to hold a given number of cubes.

2B Patterns from the Bottom Up   PAIRS

Students solve problems on More Boxes from the Bottom Up (M33–M35).

For complete details about this activity, see Session 3.3, page 81.

2C Boxes to Hold 16 Cubes   INDIVIDUALS PAIRS

Explain to students that this activity is like the one they did in Session 3.3 when they made patterns for open boxes to hold 12 cubes, only this time they will be making boxes to hold 16 cubes.

As with the 12-cube box patterns, there are a number of different boxes that students can make to solve this problem. There are two different boxes that will contain the 1 × 4 × 4 cube configuration. One has a 1 × 4 open top; the other has a 4 × 4 open top.

Similarly, there are two boxes that contain a 2 × 2 × 4 cube configuration: one with a 2 × 4 open top and one with a 2 × 2 open top.

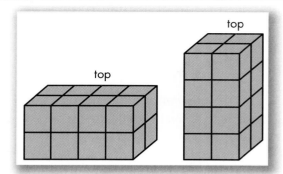

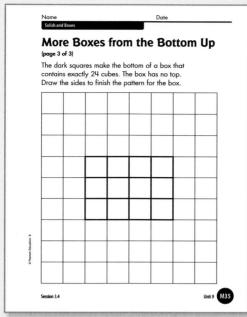

In addition, there are two boxes with a 1 × 1 × 16 configuration and three boxes with a 1 × 2 × 8 configuration (not pictured).

Students work alone or in pairs on this activity. Either way, each student should have a supply of grid paper to search for patterns. To find boxes that hold 16 cubes, students draw their ideas for patterns on Three-Quarter-Inch Grid Paper (M27), cut them out, fold them, and then fill them with cubes. Patterns that work should be taped together into boxes and saved.

Encourage students to make their boxes out of whole sheets of paper when they can rather than separate pieces. Explain that some boxes for 16 cubes will require that they tape several sheets of paper together.

ONGOING ASSESSMENT: Observing Students at Work

Students use visualization skills to design boxes to hold rectangular prisms containing 16 cubes.

- **What strategies are students using to design a box to hold 16 cubes?** Do they think about layers? Do they use knowledge of factors of 16 to help them conceptualize their boxes?

- **Do they work with different configurations of 16 cubes, or are they making multiple patterns for the same configuration?** Are they designing boxes with different open faces for the same configuration?

DIFFERENTIATION: Supporting the Range of Learners

Intervention For students who are having difficulty, you might suggest that they build a rectangular structure from 16 cubes first, place it on the grid, and try to draw the pattern for the box. Give students plenty of time to devise multiple solutions.

Help them think about how many layers are in the cube structure they made and how they can show those layers in the box pattern.

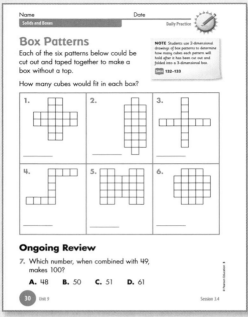

▲ Student Activity Book, p. 30

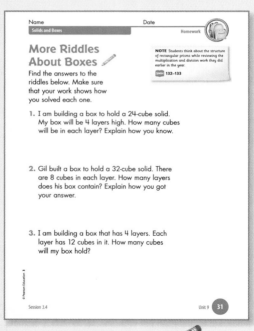

▲ Student Activity Book, p. 31

How many cubes are in the bottom layer of your box? How many layers are there? How can you show the bottom and layers in your pattern?

Extension Students who quickly find patterns for one configuration of 16 cubes positioned with different open tops can be encouraged to try a different configuration of 16 cubes. If a student has successfully made boxes with different open faces for a $1 \times 4 \times 4$ arrangement, ask this question:

Is there a different rectangular prism that you can make with 16 cubes? What boxes can you make for that prism?

SESSION FOLLOW-UP

3 Daily Practice and Homework

 Daily Practice: For reinforcement of this unit's content, have students complete *Student Activity Book* page 30.

Homework: Students solve problems on *Student Activity Book* page 31. Give two copies of Three-Quarter-Inch Grid Paper (M27) to each student. Explain that this *Student Activity Book* page 31 contains three riddles about boxes that hold cubes that are like the ones students solved in the Math Workshop. Let them know that the use of grid paper is optional, although some may find it helpful to make the boxes described in each problem.

Student Math Handbook: Students and families may use *Student Math Handbook* pages 132–133 for reference and review. See pages 115–117 in the back of this unit.

End-of-Unit Assessment

Math Focus Points

◆ Describing the components and properties of different classes of solids such as polyhedra (3-D shapes having only flat surfaces, such as prisms and pyramids) and nonpolyhedra (such as cones and cylinders)

◆ Determining the number of cubes that will fit in the box made by a given pattern

◆ Designing patterns for boxes that will hold a given number of cubes

Today's Plan		Materials
① ASSESSMENT ACTIVITY **End-of-Unit Assessment**	✓ 🕐 👤 60 MIN INDIVIDUALS	• M36–M40, End-of-Unit Assessment* • Connecting cubes; geometric solids (from Session 1.1; as needed)
② DISCUSSION **Solutions to the Assessment Problems**	👥 CLASS	
③ SESSION FOLLOW-UP **Daily Practice**		• *Student Activity Book,* pp. 33–34 • *Student Math Handbook,* pp. 129–130, 132–133

*See *Materials to Prepare,* p. 67.

Ten-Minute Math

Quick Images: 3D Show Images 13 and 14 (one at a time) from *Quick Images* (T106), and follow the procedure for the basic routine. For each image, students discuss how they built their structures, including any revisions they made after each viewing. Ask questions such as:

• How did you remember the parts of the image?

• What did you notice about the relationship of the parts of the image?

• What helped you remember the whole image, so you could build your structure?

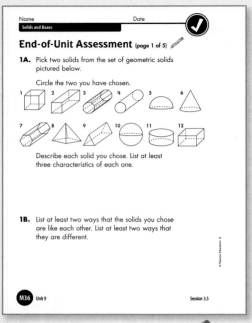

▲ **Resource Masters, M36** PORTFOLIO WRITING

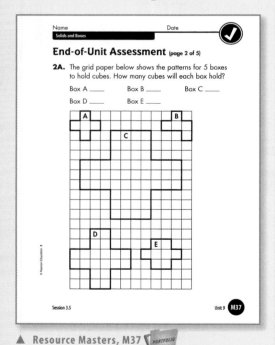

Name _____ Date _____

Solids and Boxes

End-of-Unit Assessment (page 2 of 5)

2A. The grid paper below shows the patterns for 5 boxes
to hold cubes. How many cubes will each box hold?

Box A _____   Box B _____   Box C _____

Box D _____   Box E _____

Session 3.5   Unit 9 M37

▲ **Resource Masters, M37** PORTFOLIO

ASSESSMENT ACTIVITY

End-of-Unit Assessment

60 MIN INDIVIDUALS

On End-of-Unit Assessment (M36–M40), students work individually to
solve three assessment problems.

In Problem 1A, students identify and describe the components of
geometric solids. In Problem 1B, students describe similarities and
differences of geometric solids. These problems address Benchmark 1:
Identify and compare the attributes of three-dimensional solids.

In Problems 2A and 2B, students determine how many cubes fit in a box
pattern. These problems address Benchmark 2: Determine the number
of cubes (volume) that will fit in the box made by a given pattern.

In Problems 3A and 3B, students create a box pattern with a given
volume. These problems address Benchmark 3: Design patterns for boxes
that will hold a given number of cubes.

ONGOING ASSESSMENT: Observing Students at Work

Students demonstrate knowledge of the components of geometric solids and the relationship between the dimensions of an open box and the volume of that box.

- **Do students accurately count the edges, faces, and vertices of the geometric solids, or are they making the mistake of counting some components more than once?** Do they correctly identify the shape of the faces?

- **Do students correctly identify what is alike and what is different about the two solids they chose?**

- **Are students able to correctly determine the number of cubes that will fit into the box made by a given pattern?** Do they consider the number of cubes that make up the bottom layer and then look at the sides to determine the number of layers?

- **Do students accurately draw the sides of a box pattern when given the bottom of the box and the number of cubes that box will hold?**

Those students who finish in less than 60 minutes can complete Math Workshop activities from Session 3.4.

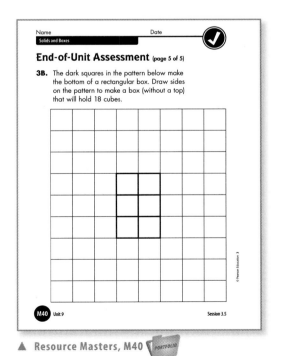

▲ Resource Masters, M40

▲ Resource Masters, M38

▲ Resource Masters, M39

Professional Development

❶ Teacher Note: End-of-Unit Assessment, p. 101

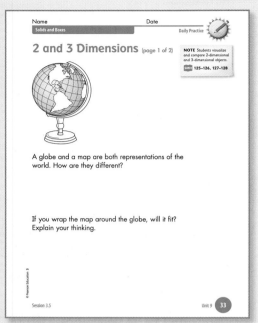

▲ Student Activity Book, p. 33

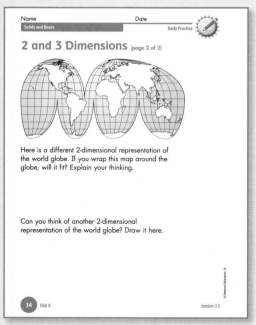

▲ Student Activity Book, p. 34

CLASS

DISCUSSION
2 Solutions to the Assessment Problems

When all students are finished with the assessment, have a class discussion about the solutions to the assessment problems.❶

SESSION FOLLOW-UP
3 Daily Practice

 Daily Practice: For enrichment, have students complete *Student Activity Book* pages 33–34.

 Student Math Handbook: Students and families may use *Student Math Handbook* pages 129–130, 132–133 for reference and review. See pages 115–117 in the back of this unit.

Professional Development

Solids and Boxes

Teacher Notes

In Part 6 of *Implementing Investigations in Grade 3,* you will find a set of Teacher Notes that addresses topics and issues applicable to the curriculum as a whole rather than to specific curriculum units. They include the following:

Computational Fluency and Place Value

Computation Algorithms and Methods

Representations and Contexts for Mathematical Work

Foundations of Algebra in the Elementary Grades

Discussing Mathematical Ideas

**Racial and Linguistic Diversity in the Classroom:
  Raising Questions About What Equity in the Math
  Classroom Means Today**

Dialogue Boxes

Geometric Solids: Types and Terminology

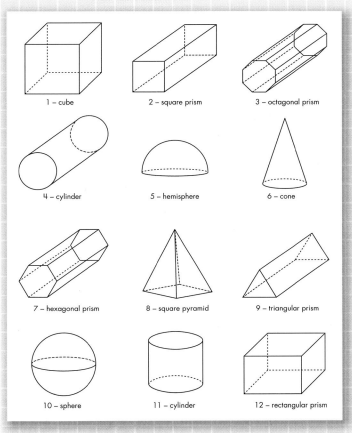

1 – cube   2 – square prism   3 – octagonal prism

4 – cylinder   5 – hemisphere   6 – cone

7 – hexagonal prism   8 – square pyramid   9 – triangular prism

10 – sphere   11 – cylinder   12 – rectangular prism

Terminology: It is not important that students memorize terminology or acquire abstract definitions for geometric solids at this grade level. However, you should use the correct terminology, along with terms used by students, to familiarize students with it. For instance, you might use the term *polyhedra* or a student-generated term such as *shapes with flat sides* interchangeably, telling students that mathematicians call these shapes *polyhedra*.

Students also frequently use *corner* or *point* for *vertex*, *line* for *edge*, and *side* for *face*. As long as they are communicating effectively, allow them to use the language they are comfortable with, while you continue to model the correct terms. Over time with repeated modeling, many third graders begin to use the correct terminology.

The terms *edge* and *face* are used in this unit, but generally *corner* and *vertex* (plural: *vertices*) are used interchangeably so that students are exposed to the correct terminology for this component.

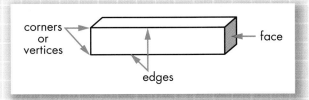

Types of Solids: There are many types of geometric solids. Several, such as spheres, cones, and cylinders (Figures 4, 5, 6, 10, and 11 above), have some curved surfaces. Others (Figures 1, 2, 3, 7, 8, 9, and 12), called polyhedra, have only flat surfaces. (*Polyhedron* means having many flat surfaces, or faces.)

Two common types of polyhedra are prisms and pyramids. Students might say that prisms (Figures 1, 2, 3, 7, 9, and 12) have "a top and bottom that are the same shape and all rectangular sides (lateral faces)." Prisms are named by the shape on "the top and bottom"; hence, Figure 7 is a hexagonal prism. Similarly, they might say that a pyramid (Figure 8) has "a flat bottom and a point for the top, with all sides triangles." Pyramids are named by the shape that is the base (flat bottom); in this case, a square.

Teacher Note

Strategies for Finding the Number of Cubes in a Box

The strategies students use to determine the number of cubes that fit in a completed box vary greatly. Some students will count the cubes that fit into the box 1 by 1. Some will count the cubes in a layer (not always a horizontal layer) and then use repeated addition or skip counting to find the total. Others will use multiplication to determine how many cubes are in a layer and then use multiplication again to find the total number of cubes.

Some students, however, will count squares. They might count squares in the pattern. Others might fill the box with cubes and then take the connected cubes out of the box and count the number of squares visible on all sides. It is essential that you help these students correctly determine the number of cubes.

The most basic and reliable method for determining the number of cubes is to count them 1 by 1 as they are taken apart. However, before students resort to this method, which they can all employ, model a more efficient method. You can separate the rectangular cube array into layers, asking students to count the cubes in a layer, and then successively stack the layers as students keep track of the total.

You should ask, "How many cubes do you think are in the bottom layer? How do you know? How many cubes are there after I add this layer? What about after I add this layer? So how many cubes are in the whole box?"

It is important that students develop their own workable strategies to solve these problems in order for them to gain the experience they need to make sense of rectangular configurations of cubes. Imposing on students any particular approach for determining the number of cubes that fit in a box may result in students learning the suggested approaches by rote.

Instead, allow class discussions and your modeling to inform students of more efficient strategies than the ones they may currently be using. For example, after a discussion of strategies, if the idea of using layers has not been mentioned, model it as described above.

Students gradually progress to more powerful ways of conceptualizing cube configurations as they have repeated experiences with using a strategy to determine the number of cubes, building boxes, filling them with cubes, counting the cubes, and discussing their ideas with classmates.

Do not expect all students to be able to think in terms of layers by the end of this investigation. They do similar work in Grades 4 and 5. It is sufficient if they have developed a procedure that gives correct answers. Despite your efforts to promote it, some students may not yet be able to arrange cubes in layers.

Do not push students to use dimensions (length × width × height = volume). Often elementary students simply memorize this formula without an understanding of why it works. Too much emphasis on this can pressure students to adopt a numerical procedure that they do not understand, causing them to abandon a visual method that does make sense to them.

Assessment: Writing About How Many Cubes

Problem

Benchmark addressed:

- **Benchmark 2:** Determine the number of cubes (volume) that will fit in the box made by a given pattern.

In order to meet the benchmark, students' work should show that they can:

- Accurately determine the number of cubes that fit in a given box pattern without filling it with cubes;

- Write explanations that clearly show how they determined the number of cubes.

The expectation is that most students will meet the benchmark for this activity, although some may need guidance correcting errors. Other students may need additional experiences to develop their understanding of the structure of box patterns and the rectangular prisms that fit inside them.

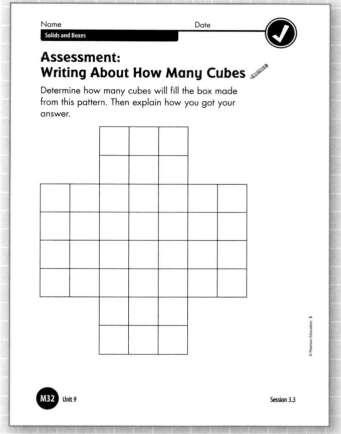

▲ Resource Masters, M32

Meeting the Benchmark

Students who meet the benchmark correctly determine the number of cubes that fill the box made from the pattern without filling the box with cubes. Their explanations demonstrate an understanding of the relationship between the number of cubes that fill the bottom of the box and the number of layers indicated by the box pattern. Adam, Beatriz, and Kim all used this relationship to predict that the box would hold 24 cubes.

Adam found the number of cubes in the bottom layer (12), looked at the sides to determine the number of layers, and then added 12 plus 12 to get 24.

> 12
> +12
> 24
> There are 12 blocks on the bodem of the cube. There are two on the side that go up. So you would do 12+12=24. That's how I got my answer.

Adam's Work

Beatriz and Kim did the same but used multiplication instead of addition to come up with 24 cubes.

> I think that the answer is 24. The reason I think that is because the sides are two layers and the middle is twelve.
> Two × 12 = 24

Beatriz's Work

> I counted the numbers in the middle and it was 12. Then I looked on the side and I counted up the sections and it was two. then what I did was multiply them together and it was 24.

Kim's Work

Keith thought about vertical rather than horizontal layers in determining the number of cubes that would fill the box. He recognized that the 6 squares on one side of the pattern represent a 2 × 3 layer of 6 cubes. He looked at the squares on the other side to determine that the box will hold 4 of these layers of 6 cubes. He then multiplied, skip counted, or added to come up with his answer of 24.

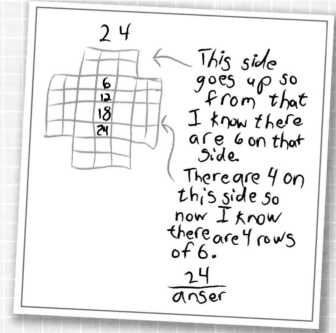

Keith's Work

Partially Meeting the Benchmark

Students whose answers demonstrate understanding of the structure of the box patterns and the prism that fits inside but who miscalculate the number of cubes partially meet the benchmark.

Jane wrote that there are 15 cubes in the middle (bottom layer) and that the box will hold 30 cubes because it is two layers high.

> On the bottom was 15 cubes.
> On the sides were 2 rows.
> So I knew that all the rows repusented a side.
> 15×2=30

Jane's Work

Arthur correctly identified the 12 cubes that form the bottom layer and the two layers of the box but wrote 26 as the total number of cubes the box will hold.

> Well Sinse they is 12 in the middle and 2 frooгs and so all you need to do is 2×12 and that =26

Arthur's Work

Ask students like Jane and Arthur to look at the box pattern again to check their answers. It is likely that these students can self-correct.

Not Meeting the Benchmark

Some students confuse the number of squares in a box pattern with the number of cubes that will fill the box, believing that a cube fits on each square and that the folded box will hold every cube.

Edwin numbered the squares in the box pattern 1–40 and determined that the box would hold 40 cubes.

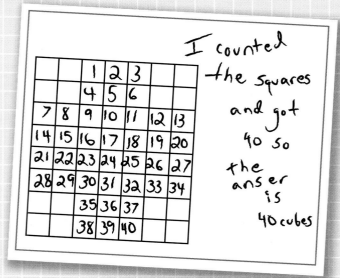

Edwin's Work

These students need help thinking about what the squares in the box pattern represent. Have these students cut out the pattern, fold the box without taping it, and fill it with cubes. This should help students see how the squares on the sides of the pattern line up with the outside faces of the cubes in the rectangular prism and that the number of rows of squares on the side represents the number of layers in the prism.

Strategies for Boxes That Hold 12 Cubes

The following discussion among students working to make their 12-cube box patterns demonstrates the range of strategies you are likely to encounter in your class.

Teacher: What methods are you using to make your boxes?

Deondra: I just drew a rectangle that had 12 squares, and then I put on the sides.

Denzel: I made a building with 12 cubes in it. Then I put it on my paper and traced the bottom. I looked at the sides of the building and could tell how to draw the sides of my box.

Elena: You count the cubes in the bottom and it has to be a factor of 12. Then for the sides, you have to do whatever that number is times that factor that makes 12. Say there were 6 in the bottom, 6 times 2 is 12, so you have to make each side go up 2 squares.

Bridget: I just sort of look at it. I draw a pattern, then fold it up to see if it works. If it doesn't work, I try again.

Consider how these different students are approaching the problem. Deondra's strategy is common. The drawback with this strategy is that it will not produce multilayer boxes. In fact, some students who use this strategy always ignore the height of the sides, discovering their error only after they attempt to fill their box with cubes.

Denzel's strategy is especially useful for students having difficulty and could be suggested to them as a good approach.

Elena's strategy is quite sophisticated—she seems to be using information she learned in the multiplication and division unit (including the term factor). In fact, it is not uncommon for students to comment that they can solve this problem "because I know my multiplication pairs."

Finally, Bridget has some difficulty expressing her strategy accurately. It might seem as though she is using random trial and error. However, because she was successful in

making several boxes, her trial and error seems to have been guided by some intuitive ideas that she either could not express or was not explicitly aware of.

Students can devise some amazingly creative patterns, especially when prompted to find more than one pattern for the same 12-cube box, as suggested for homework. The diagram below shows two different patterns students made for the 1 × 1 × 12 box.

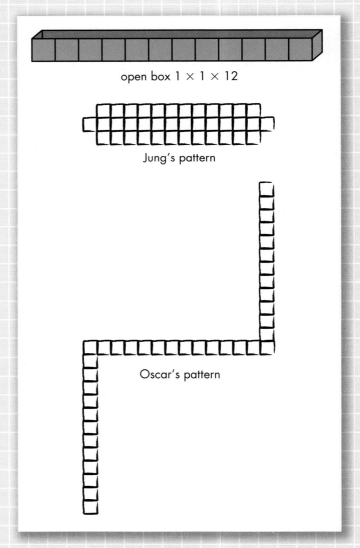

open box 1 × 1 × 12

Jung's pattern

Oscar's pattern

End-of-Unit Assessment

Problem 1A

Benchmark addressed:

Benchmark 1: Identify and compare attributes of 3-dimensional solids.

In order to meet the benchmark, students' work should show that they can:

- Correctly list at least three components of each solid.

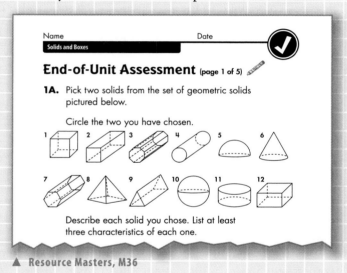

▲ **Resource Masters, M36**

Meeting the Benchmark

Students who meet the benchmark correctly list three or more components of each of the chosen solids. They may count faces, edges, and vertices and name the shape of the faces. Note that use of the terms *side* for *face* and *corner* or *point* for *vertex* is acceptable.

Jane chose the cube and the square pyramid.

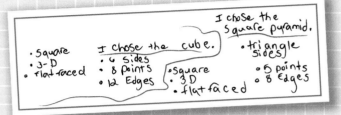

Jane's Work

She correctly identified the cube as having 6 "sides," 8 "points," 12 edges, and only flat faces. She correctly identified the square pyramid as having 5 "points," 8 edges, only flat faces, and triangular faces.

Partially Meeting the Benchmark

These students correctly list at least two components of each shape but may make errors when listing other components. For example, they may incorrectly count the vertices or edges.

Bridget chose the hexagonal prism and the square pyramid. She correctly identified the hexagonal prism as having "8 sides" and "12 points" but incorrectly counted the number of edges as 6 instead of 18. She correctly identified the square pyramid as having "5 sides, 5 points, and 8 edges."

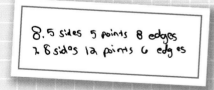

Bridget's Work

Adam chose the cube and the square pyramid. He correctly identified the cube as a polyhedron and listed two characteristics: "6 sides and 6 squares put together." He also correctly identified the square pyramid as a polyhedron. However, he did not list three correct components of that solid, identifying it as having 6 faces instead of 5 and as being composed of 3 triangles (instead of 4) and 1 square.

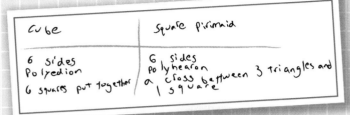

Adam's Work

Work with students like Bridget who incorrectly count the edges (or other components) of a solid to make sure that they understand the terms. Help them develop effective ways of keeping track of the components as they count to make sure that they count them all or do not double-count any component.

Students like Adam may be able to self-correct if given the opportunity to check their work.

Not Meeting the Benchmark

Students who are unable to list at least two correct components of each solid do not meet the benchmark for Problem 1A. These students need more practice working with the set of geometric solids and can benefit by playing *What's My Shape?* outside math time when possible. Make time to review the components (faces, edges, and vertices) with these students and keep the solids available for their use.

Problem 1B

Benchmark addressed:

Benchmark 1: Identify and compare attributes of 3-dimensional solids.

In order to meet the benchmark, students' work should show that they can:

• Correctly list at least one attribute that the chosen solids share and one way in which they differ.

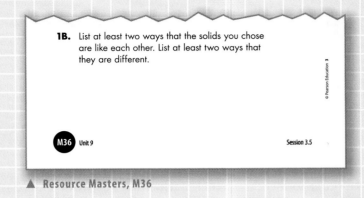

▲ Resource Masters, M36

Meeting the Benchmark

These students attend to the attributes of each solid to correctly list one or more things the solids have in common and one or more ways in which they differ.

Oscar chose the cube and the rectangular prism and wrote the following:

"They both have six sides that are all flat. They're different because the cube has square sides and the other one has rectangular sides."

Keith chose the cube and square pyramid and wrote the following:

"They both have no round sides. They both have at least one square. They're different because one (pyramid) has 5 corners and 5 sides and the other (cube) has 8 corners and 6 sides."

Keisha chose the cone and square pyramid and wrote the following:

"Both have a vertex on top. Number 8 (pyramid) has straight edges and number 6 (cone) does not."

Partially Meeting the Benchmark

These students attend to the attributes of the solids to correctly list one or more ways that the two solids are alike, but they do not correctly list at least one way they are different (or vice versa).

Benjamin chose the cube and square pyramid and correctly wrote that they are the same because they both have a "flat square on the bottom and flat sides." However, for the way in which the solids differ he wrote the following:

"They have different names."

Not Meeting the Benchmark

These students do not correctly list one similarity and one difference between the chosen solids that have to do with the attributes of each shape. Some students, for example, still describe geometric solids by what they look like rather than by identifying their attributes.

Gina chose the cone and the cube and wrote the following:

"One looks like a TP [tepee] and one looks like a box."

Students like Gina need more practice identifying the individual components of each solid and the characteristics that make each one resemble the named object. Ask them questions such as the following: "What if I had never seen a tepee? Tell me what characteristics of the cone make it look like a tepee. What about the cube? Why does it look like a box?"

Problems 2A and 2B

Benchmark addressed:

Benchmark 2: Determine the number of cubes (volume) that will fit in the box made by a given pattern.

In order to meet the benchmark, students' work should show that they can:

• Accurately determine the number of cubes that fit in given box patterns;

• Write explanations that clearly show how they made their determinations.

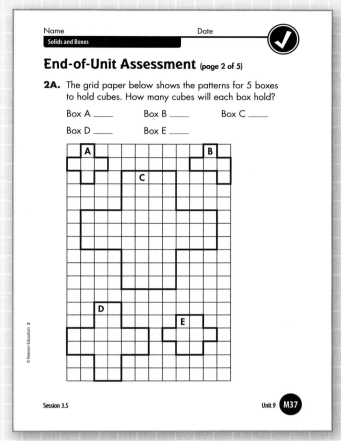

▲ **Resource Masters, M37**

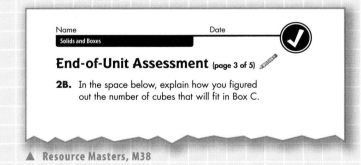

▲ **Resource Masters, M38**

Meeting the Benchmark

Students who meet the benchmark correctly determine the number of cubes that fill the boxes made from the patterns in Problem 2A. Their explanations in Problem 2B demonstrate an understanding of the relationship between the number of cubes that fill the bottom of the box and the number of layers indicated by the box pattern.

Pilar clearly explained that she counted the number of squares in the middle of the pattern, determined the number of layers, and multiplied 12 by 3 to correctly determine that the box would hold 36 cubes.

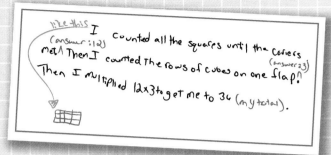

Pilar's Work

Partially Meeting the Benchmark

Students whose answers demonstrate understanding of the structure of the box pattern and the prism that fits inside but who miscalculate the number of cubes partially meet the benchmark.

Elena counted the 12 squares in the bottom layer and identified the number of layers as 3, but miscalculated the product as 48.

> I counted the squares in the middle (12) then x it by three. (48)
> 12×2 = 36+10 = 46+2 = 48

Elena's Work

Ask students like Elena to look at the box pattern again to check their answers. It is likely that these students can self-correct.

Not Meeting the Benchmark

It is possible, though not likely, that some students may still confuse the number of squares in a box pattern with the number of cubes that will fill the box, believing that a cube fits on each square and that the folded box will hold every cube.

Philip added the top and bottom flaps of the box (12 + 12) to get 24, the two side flaps (9 + 9) to get 18, combined the sums to get 42, and then added the squares in the middle (42 + 12) to get a total of 54. Other students may arrive at an answer of 54 by counting each square in the pattern.

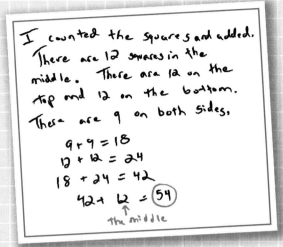

Philip's Work

These students need help thinking about what the squares in the box pattern represent. Have these students cut out the pattern, fold the box without taping it, and fill it with cubes. This should help students see how the squares on the sides of the pattern line up with the outside faces of the cubes in the rectangular prism and that the number of rows of squares on the sides represent the number of layers in the prism.

Problems 3A and 3B

Benchmark addressed:

Benchmark 3: Design patterns for boxes that will hold a given number of cubes.

In order to meet the benchmark, students' work should show that they can:

- Correctly draw the sides of a box pattern to hold a given number of cubes when given the bottom of the box.

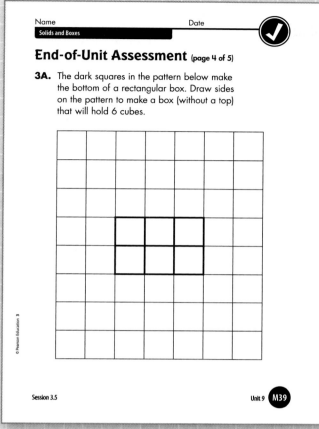

▲ Resource Masters, M39

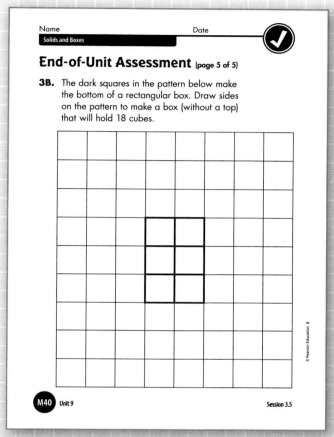

▲ Resource Masters, M40

Because of the nature of this assessment, students either meet or do not meet the benchmark. There is no "partially meets the benchmark."

Meeting the Benchmark

Students who meet the benchmark for Problem 3A, Box A draw the sides to make a box pattern that will hold 1 layer of 6 cubes. For Problem 3B, Box B, they draw the sides to make a box pattern that will hold 3 layers of 6 cubes. Note that although most students are likely to draw the "cross" type pattern for each box, other patterns can be made that will hold the given number of cubes.

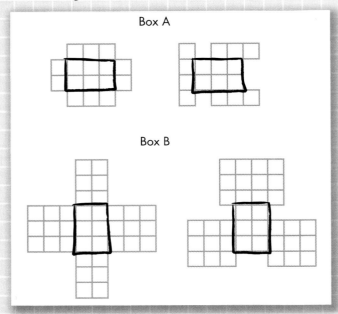

Box A

Box B

Not Meeting the Benchmark

Some students may incorrectly draw the sides of the patterns, resulting in boxes that do not hold the given number of cubes. These students may still need to make the cube configurations to fit the box first. For example, for Problem 3B, they would start by making a 3×2 rectangle of 6 cubes and placing it on the 3×2 pattern for the bottom of the box. Ask questions to help them build the rest of the rectangular prism. "How many cubes have you used so far? If this box will hold 18 cubes, how many more layers of 6 do you need?"

When the prism is complete, ask them to draw the sides of the box. If they do not see how to proceed, point to one of the lateral sides of the structure and ask, "How tall is the structure? How many layers are there? How many cubes do you see on this side? Can you draw this side on the paper?"

Repeat these questions for the other sides as necessary.

Talking to Students About Sorting

As students are sorting geometric solids in Session 1.1, this teacher stops to talk with a small group of students. She notices that they have sorted the solids into polyhedra and nonpolyhedra. She points to the polyhedra.

Teacher: How are the shapes in this group the same?

Denzel: The sides are all different. Some are rectangles, here are triangles, and some are squares. These are rectangles even though they are really skinny.

The teacher notes that this student is focusing on what is different about the shapes in this group rather than what is the same.

Kathryn: They have points and edges and are flat. This group (nonpolyhedra) doesn't have them.

Teacher: What do you mean?

Kathryn: [referring to a table to illustrate]: This is a point [touching a corner of the table]. This is the edge [touching an edge of the table]. It's flat [placing hand down on the top of the table].

The teacher points to the polyhedra.

Teacher: If I had a shape that I wanted to add to this collection, what would it have to look like?

Students: The same thing.

Teacher: What do you mean by the same thing? What characteristics would a shape need to belong in this group?

Oscar: It would need corners, and sides. Because this one (cone) is not in the group. It has a corner and the bottom is flat, but it doesn't have sides that are flat. The sides are round here.

Later, during the whole class discussion, the teacher removes the nonpolyhedra from the set of solids and introduces the idea of sorting the polyhedra into pyramids and prisms.

Teacher: Now I'm going to sort these into two groups. [The teacher sorts the polyhedra into two groups: prisms and pyramids.]

Teacher: How are the shapes in the two groups different?

Elena: This one [points to pyramid], when it goes up it gets thinner. All the others [points to prisms] stay the same shape.

Teacher: Elena pointed to this group (prisms) and said that they "stay the same shape." What do you think she means by that?

Kenji: If you look at this one [picks up hexagonal prism], the top and bottom are both the same shape. They're both hexagons. On this one (square prism), the top and bottom are both squares.

Pilar: I noticed something else. On these (the prisms), the sides are rectangles and on this one (the pyramid), the sides are triangles.

The teacher holds up the triangular prism.

Teacher: This figure is triangular in shape. Why isn't it in the group with this one, the pyramid?

Kenji: It's kind of like what Elena said before. This one (pyramid) has a point on top, so it doesn't have as many sides. This (triangular prism) has a top and a bottom, just like the other shapes in this group (prisms).

As students work through ideas about what distinguishes polyhedra from nonpolyhedra, the teacher's questions encourage them to describe which components of the shapes differentiate one group from the other. Later, in the whole class discussion focusing on the difference between prisms and pyramids, the teacher again asks questions to help students be increasingly precise in their descriptions.

Playing *What's My Shape?*

To introduce the game *What's My Shape?*, the teacher first acts as the Chooser, responding to students' questions with yes or no answers while also trying to help clarify and correct their questioning.

Teacher: I'm ready for your first question.

Bridget: Does it roll?

Teacher: Yes. So what shape can it be? Keisha, why don't you put aside the shapes that won't work? The rest of you say whether you agree with her.

Keisha puts all the polyhedra into the box. She also puts the hemisphere away.

Jane: Wait. That one rolls.

Keisha: How?

Jane goes to the front of the room and demonstrates.

Teacher: What do you think? Should the hemisphere go in the box? [Most students say no.] Let's have another question.

Benjamin: Does your shape come to a point?

Teacher: What do you mean by a point?

Benjamin: It's like the top, a sharp part.

Teacher: No, my shape does not come to a point.

One student removes the cone and puts it in the box.

Gil: Does your shape have a circle on the bottom?

Teacher: Yes, it does have a circle on the bottom.

The students keep the cylinders and the hemisphere and remove the remaining figures.

Edwin: Does it look like a coffee can?

Teacher: Can someone say something about the last question?

Dwayne: Edwin asked what it looked like in real life. You can't do that in this game.

Teacher: Let's think about what Edwin was asking. What does a coffee can look like? Is there another question Edwin can ask to find the information he was looking for?

Pilar: Is your shape short and wide?

Teacher: Yes, it is. Can we put away any more shapes?

Denzel: We can put this one away because it's not short and wide.

Denzel removes the tall cylinder and places it in the box. The short cylinder and hemisphere remain.

Teacher: I think we can do this with one more question.

Becky: Does your shape have a circle on the bottom and the top?

Teacher: Yes, it does. Only the short cylinder and hemisphere are still out of the box. Which one is my shape?

Keith: It has to be the short cylinder. The other one only has a circle on the bottom, not the top.

Throughout this demonstration game, the teacher encourages students to ask questions that focus on the characteristics of the geometric solids. She pushes Benjamin to define what he means by point. When Edwin asks whether the shape "looks like a coffee can," she asks students to think about the characteristics Edwin is looking for in order to reword his question. In addition, as she responds to and clarifies their questions, she models using terminology (e.g., referring to the hemisphere and cylinders by name).

Building Common Vocabulary

During one game of *What's My Shape?*, a student asks a question about the number of edges of a solid. The teacher notices that not all students are using the term *edge* to mean the same thing and tries to bring this to students' attention. She shows a triangular prism standing on one of its bases.

Teacher: How many edges would you say this has?

Arthur: Three. [points to the top three edges]

Teacher: Do you all agree?

Jung and Nancy: Yeah. Three.

Denzel: Six. Three on the top and three on the bottom.

Jung: I'll change mine to five.

Teacher: It seems like we have a few different answers to this question. Can anyone explain to us how you arrived at your answer?

Denzel: I would like to change my answer to nine.

Teacher: All right, Denzel. Can you tell us how you came up with 9?

Denzel: [Pointing to each edge] This one has 1, 2, 3 on the bottom; 4, 5, 6 around the side; 7, 8, 9 on the top.

Teacher: Do you all understand Denzel's explanation?

Most students switch their answers to nine.

Arthur: I still think it's three. Edges of tables are on top.

Denzel: Edges are sharp. See, the edges on the side and bottom [running his fingers along the side and bottom edges of the triangular prism] are sharp, just like the top. They're just like the edges on this desk [pointing to the teacher's desk].

Teacher: What do you think, class? Can we agree on what *edge* means?

Jung: I think Denzel's right. All of them are edges, so there's nine.

Arthur: Oh—I see that now.

In this discussion, the teacher uses students' own observations about a triangular prism to help them come to a common understanding of the term *edge*. At the end of this discussion, not only do most of the students agree that the triangular prism has nine edges, but they also share an understanding of this important geometric term that will aid their communication as they continue to investigate and classify geometric shapes. As confusion or disagreements about other terms arise, more conversations like this one may be needed.

Patterns for Cubes

Students in this classroom have just completed Patterns for Cube Boxes (M15). This excerpt from the class discussion illustrates some of the ways they try to convince their classmates of their answers.

Teacher: Let's talk about which patterns on the sheet make an open box for a cube.

Elena: The answer to the first one (Pattern A) is No.

Teacher: What if I weren't sure about that? How can you convince me that it won't work?

Elena: All you have to do is fold this up in your mind. There aren't any sides to it.

Teacher: Do you all agree?

The students indicate their agreement.

Bridget: You could fold it on top of itself, but you couldn't cover the whole thing.

Oscar: It's like a tunnel.

Teacher: What do you think about Pattern C?

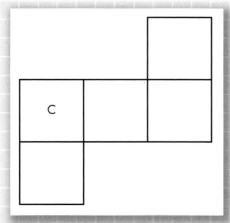

Nancy: I don't think it works.

Gil: I think it does. Can I show her? [He comes up to the overhead projector and points at the pattern on the transparency.] Look. Pretend there's a cube in the middle. You fold this side up. Then you fold the other side up. Then you fold over the extra ones that stick out.

Teacher: Pattern D looks interesting. Will it work?

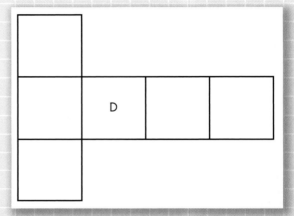

Jung: Not if you want to make an open box.

Nicholas: Yeah. It has a top.

Teacher: How do you know that this box will have a top?

Philip: It has six squares. It should have five.

Teacher: Can someone say more about why it should have five squares?

Beatriz: Remember that we talked before about how a cube has six square faces. If the box has six squares, it will cover the whole cube. It won't be open.

Teacher: What about Pattern E?

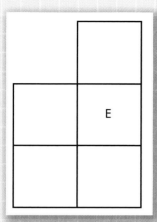

Kim: [comes to the overhead] No way. If you put it (the cube) here, anywhere you put it, it would not work. Like there. You fold this up and then you fold this up, what would you do with this square? This one? This one?

The teacher in this classroom has specific questions in mind as she conducts this discussion. Are some students able to visualize the folded box without the cube present? Do others need to use a cube to visualize the results of folding the pattern? Do students understand that the open box pattern must contain five squares because a cube has six square faces?

During the discussion, she asks questions that push students to elaborate on their thinking about which patterns will or will not make an open box for a single cube. For example, when Elena states that Pattern A will not work, the teacher asks Elena to convince her. When Jung and Nicholas state that Pattern D will make a closed box, she asks them how they know this. When Philip points out that the pattern should have five squares instead of six, she asks for an explanation of why this is true. Asking for such elaborations supports students in expressing their ideas, and provides information for any students for whom these ideas are less familiar.

Dialogue Box

Making Patterns for the 2-Cube Solid

Dwayne and Jung are working together to create patterns for open boxes to hold a 2-cube solid. They have made one pattern.

Now their teacher is encouraging them to find more patterns for the same shape.

Teacher: That's good. How did you think of that pattern?

Dwayne: It's like the cross pattern we made for one cube.

Teacher: Good thinking. Do you think there are any more patterns for two cubes?

Both students hesitate.

Teacher: There were quite a few patterns for a single cube.

Dwayne: But that was different. There are two cubes now. [He draws a new pattern.]

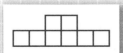

Jung: Yeah, that works. And you can have another pattern if you just move these over. [She indicates moving the top two squares from positions 3 and 4 to positions 4 and 5 in the row of six squares. She then draws and cuts out the following pattern.]

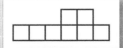

Dwayne: Here's another one.

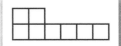

Teacher: Do you think there are any others?

Dwayne and Jung: I don't think so. [The students seem to be focused on their "move the two squares" strategy and cannot readily see other possibilities.]

Teacher I noticed that you are positioning the cubes so that the open top is two cubes across. What if you put the cubes like this?

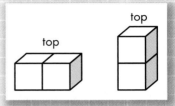

Teacher: Are there different patterns you can make now?

Jung: Maybe we can make another cross pattern.

Dwayne: Yeah, it would look like this. [Dwayne draws a new pattern.]

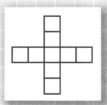

Teacher: That works. Keep looking for more.

As this teacher talks with Jung and Dwayne, he uses their experience making boxes to hold one cube to encourage them to come up with additional box patterns for the 2-cube solid. When the students seem focused on their "move the two squares" strategy and unable to readily see other possibilities, the teacher decides to present a new challenge and asks them to consider boxes that can be made with a 1-square open top.

Seeing Cube Buildings in Our Minds

In order to form a mental image of the cube structures on *Quick Images,* some students may see the image as a whole ("a box, three cubes long and two cubes high") or some may decompose it into memorable parts ("a backward L shape, 3 high and 4 across plus one row of 4 sticking forward"). The students in this classroom are discussing how they constructed the *Quick Images* pictured below. As students look for meaningful ways to see each image, the teacher encourages each student to explain how he or she visualized the image to remember it and reconstruct it.

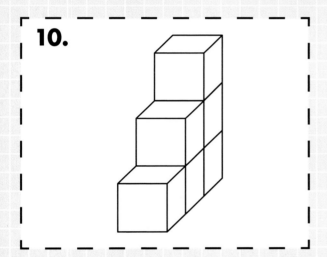

10.

Teacher: How did you see the cube building in your mind?

Elena: Three cubes going this way, two this way [motioning with hands], 1 in the middle.

Teacher: When you say "two this way," which cubes do you mean?

Elena: I mean the two in the back, going up.

Jung: I sort of did the same thing. I thought of it as 3, 2, 1—3 on the bottom, 2 in the middle, and 1 on top.

Nicholas: I pretended it was a backward L with a box in the middle.

Gil: I thought of it like steps.

Pilar: If you turn it this way, it looks like a flower.

Teacher: What did you look for when I showed the picture the second time?

Ines: Where it turns.

Kenji: How many blocks are on the arms.

Teacher: How did you know how many blocks to use for this part [indicates longest arm]?

Adam: I counted.

Keisha: I could just see it.

As students share their strategies for visualizing and building this *Quick Image,* the teacher is able to note the different ways that students organize cube structures. Elena and Jung decompose the structure into different parts and count. Nicholas sees simpler geometric shapes, such as an L (a right angle) and a box (a square). Gil and Pilar see the image as a whole object (steps and a flower).

The teacher recognizes the importance of having students discuss their strategies and knows that hearing one another's descriptions will help students try those methods and thus expand their own methods for organizing visual information.

Student Math Handbook

The *Student Math Handbook* pages related to this unit are pictured on the following pages. This book is designed to be used flexibly: as a resource for students doing classwork, as a book students can take home for reference while doing homework and playing math games with their families, and as a reference for families to better understand the work their children are doing in class.

When students take the *Student Math Handbook* home, they and their families can discuss these pages together to reinforce or enhance students' understanding of the mathematical concepts and games in this unit.

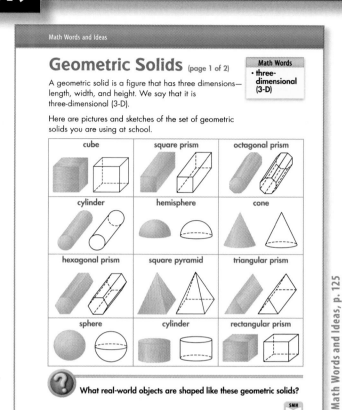

◀ Math Words and Ideas, p. 125

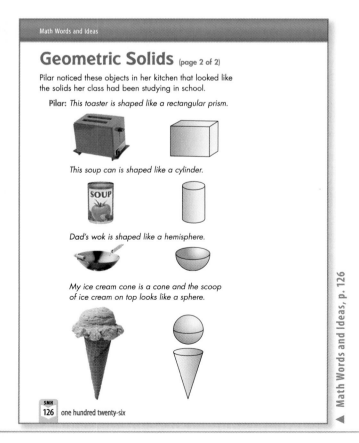

◀ Math Words and Ideas, p. 126

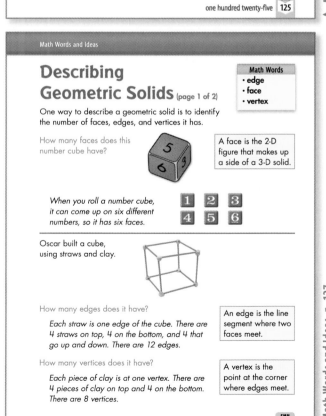

◀ Math Words and Ideas, p. 127

Describing Geometric Solids (page 2 of 2)

The square pyramid has 5 faces. There is 1 square on the bottom, and there are 4 triangles around the sides.

It has 5 vertices. There are 4 around the bottom and 1 point on top.

It has 8 edges. It took 4 straws to make the square on the bottom. And there are 4 more straws connecting to the top.

We couldn't build the cylinder with straws and clay because the edges are round, not straight, and it doesn't have any corners.

The cylinder has 3 surfaces. There is a circle on the top and a circle on the bottom. The middle part is curved—if you open it up it is a rectangle, like the label on a soup can.

 Imagine building this prism with straws and clay. How many faces does it have? What do the faces look like? How many edges does it have? How many vertices does it have?

SMH 128 one hundred twenty-eight

◀ Math Words and Ideas, p. 128

Sorting Geometric Solids (page 1 of 2)

Math Words • polyhedron

Kenji and Bridget are sorting their set of geometric solids into groups. They have found two categories.

Solids With Some Curved Surfaces

Kenji: Each of these solids can roll on the table.

Bridget: The cone has a flat circle on the bottom, but the rest of it is curved.

Solids With All Flat Faces

Kenji: Each face is a polygon.

Bridget: None of these faces are curved.

A polyhedron is a geometric solid that has all flat faces.

one hundred twenty-nine SMH 129

◀ Math Words and Ideas, p. 129

Sorting Geometric Solids (page 2 of 2)

Keith and Kelley found a different way to sort the geometric solids that they built with straws and clay.

Prisms

Keith: The top and bottom of each prism match: hexagon and hexagon, triangle and triangle, square and square.

Kelley: The faces on the sides of these prisms are all rectangles.

Pyramids

Keith: The base of each pyramid is a polygon. There is a point at the top of each pyramid.

Kelley: The faces on the sides of the pyramids are all triangles.

 Some prisms have parallelograms that are not rectangles on the sides. Can you imagine what one of these might look like?

SMH 130 one hundred thirty

◀ Math Words and Ideas, p. 130

Nets

Math Words • net

A net is a 2-D pattern that can be folded to make a 3-D figure.

Adam designed a net to cover a square pyramid.

	side	
side	bottom	side
	side	

Adam: My net has 5 polygons because the square pyramid has 5 faces.

Ines and Gil designed nets to cover a cube.

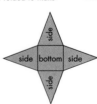

Ines's design:

	side		
side	bottom	side	top
	side		

Gil's design:

	top		
side	side	side	side
	bottom		

Ines and Gil: Since the cube has 6 square faces, each of our nets has 6 squares.

Here is a folded pattern for an open box that will hold one cube. Design a pattern with 5 squares that will make this open box.

one hundred thirty-one SMH 131

◀ Math Words and Ideas, p. 131

How Many Cubes in a Box? (page 1 of 2)

Beatriz and Denzel solved this problem.

Here is a pattern to make an open box. How many cubes will fit exactly in this box?

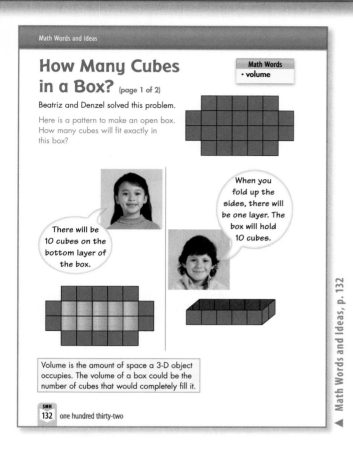

Math Words
· volume

There will be 10 cubes on the bottom layer of the box.

When you fold up the sides, there will be one layer. The box will hold 10 cubes.

Volume is the amount of space a 3-D object occupies. The volume of a box could be the number of cubes that would completely fill it.

SMH 132 one hundred thirty-two

▲ Math Words and Ideas, p. 132

How Many Cubes in a Box? (page 2 of 2)

Nicholas solved this problem.

This is the bottom of an open box that will hold exactly 30 cubes. Draw the sides to complete the pattern for the box.

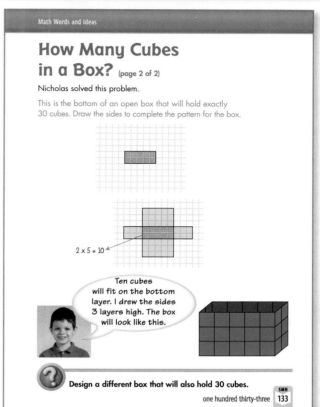

$2 \times 5 = 10$

Ten cubes will fit on the bottom layer. I drew the sides 3 layers high. The box will look like this.

? Design a different box that will also hold 30 cubes.

one hundred thirty-three **SMH 133**

▲ Math Words and Ideas, p. 133